The Sheep Brain:
A Photographic Series

C.H. Vanderwolf and Richard K. Cooley

Second Edition

A.J. Kirby Co.
London, Ontario, Canada

ISBN 0-920700-03-9

Acknowledgements

We thank the following: Mr. J. Orphan for his assistance in
sectioning the sheep head; Mr. D. Inchley for the gift of a cat brain;
Dr. R.W. Doty for the gift of a rhesus monkey brain; and the staff of the
Department of Administrative Systems, Information Centre, University
of Western Ontario for their help and the use of their computer.

Published by: **A.J. Kirby Co.**
London, Ontario
Canada N6H 5C4

Printed in Canada, by Dobbyn Creative Printing, London, Ontario.

THE SHEEP BRAIN: A PHOTOGRAPHIC SERIES

C. H. VANDERWOLF AND RICHARD K. COOLEY

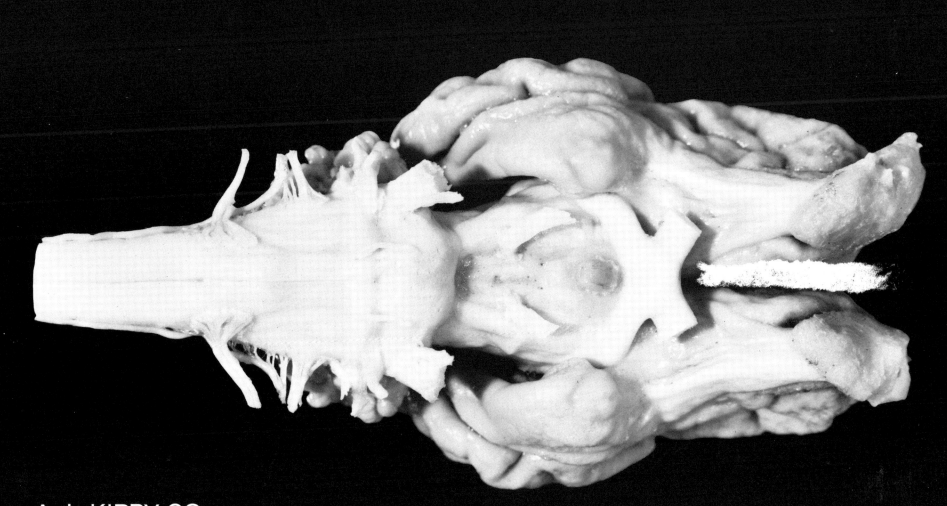

A.J. KIRBY CO.

Contents

Introduction   **7**

Methods   **8**

Terminology   **9**

References   **10-11**

Whole brain and gross dissections

Parasagittal secton of the head of a lamb   **15**

Dorsal view of the sheep brain   **16**

Lateral view of the sheep brain   **17**

Ventral view of the sheep brain   **18**

Rostral view of the cerebellum following section of the pons   **19**

Caudal view of the cerebellum   **20**

Sagittal section of the sheep brain   **21**

Sagittal section of the sheep brain showing additional details   **22**

Dorsal view of the hippocampal formation and caudate nucleus   **23**

View of lateral brainstem and the medial hippocampal formation   **24**

Dorsal view of the brainstem, diencephalon and striatum   **25**

Dissection showing the internal capsule and corona radiata   **26**

Contents

Cross sections

Cutting guide for preparing horizontal and coronal sections   **28**

Level A. Horizontal section at the level of the pineal body   **29**

Level B. Horizontal section at a ventral level of the thalamus   **30**

Level C. Coronal section caudal to the olfactory bulbs   **31**

Level D. Coronal section through the olfactory tubercle   **32**

Level E. Coronal section through the optic chiasm   **33**

Level F. Coronal section near the caudal limit of the optic chiasm   **34**

Level G. Coronal section through the mammillary body   **35**

Level H. Coronal section through the cerebral peduncle   **36**

Level I. Coronal section through the rostral pons   **37**

Level J. Coronal section through the middle of the pons   **38**

Level K. Coronal section through the rostral medulla   **39**

Level L. Coronal section just rostral to the glossopharyngeal nerve   **40**

Contents

Appendix I: Brains of common laboratory animals

    Dorsal view of the rat central nervous system   **42**

    Dorsal view of the cat brain   **43**

    Lateral view of the cat brain   **44**

    Sagittal section of the cat brain   **45**

    Dorsal view of the rhesus monkey brain   **46**

    Lateral view of the rhesus monkey brain   **47**

    Sagittal section of the rhesus monkey brain   **48**

Contents

Appendix II: Microscopic Structure of the Nervous System

Figure 1. Dog spinal cord, cross section, sacral level.   **50**

Figure 2. Dog spinal cord, cross section, lumbar level.   **51**

Figure 3. Dog spinal cord, cross section, thoracic level.   **52**

Figure 4. Dog spinal cord, cross section, cervical level.   **53**

Figure 5. Ventral horn cells from monkey spinal cord. Silver stain.   **54**

Figure 6. Spinal dorsal root ganglion.   **55**

Figure 7. Fibers of peripheral nerve, teased apart. Myelin stain.   **56**

Figure 8. Peripheral nerve, cross section. Myelin stain.   **57**

Figure 9. Section showing two types of cortex in cat brain.   **58**

Figure 10. Pyramidal cells and processes in cerebral cortex.   **59**

Figure 11. Cross section through a folium of cerebellar cortex. Nissl stain.   **60**

Figure 12.   Purkinje cells in cerebellar cortex. Golgi preparation.   **61**

Figure 13.   Astrocytes.   **62**

Figure 14. Cross section of a monkey eye.   **63**

Figure 15. Retina, choroid and sclera of monkey eye.   **64**

Figure 16. Cross-section of the cochlea, parallel to the modiolus.   **65**

Figure 17. Pacinian corpuscle.   **66**

Contents

Appendix III: Brain circuits

Introduction   **69**

    Figure 1. Somatosensory afferents: The dorsal column pathway.   **70-71**

    Figure 2. Somatosensory afferents: The spinothalamic pathway.   **72-73**

    Figure 3. Somatosensory afferents: The trigeminal pathways.   **74-75**

    Figure 4. Descending pathways for gross movements of the head, trunk, hip and shoulder.   **76-77**

    Figure 5. Descending pathways for fine movements of the extremities.   **78-79**

    Figure 6. Localization of function in the neocortex of the sheep.   **80-81**

    Figure 7. Neuronal circuits involving the cerebellum.   **82-83**

    Figure 8. Neuronal circuits involving the basal ganglia.   **84-85**

    Figure 9. Auditory pathways.   **86-87**

    Figure 10. Visual pathways.   **88-89**

    Figure 11. Taste pathways.   **90-91**

    Figure 12. Olfactory pathways.   **92-93**

    Figure 13.   Hippocampal formation.   **94-95**

    Figure 14. A cross section of the hippocampus.   **96-97**

    Figure 15. A paper model of the hippocampus.   **98-99**

    Figure 16. Schematic representation of the human cortex.   **100-101**

    Figure 17. Localization of function in the human cerebral cortex.   **102-103**

    Figure 18. Autonomic nervous system.   **104-105**

Introduction

In the late 20th century we appear to be in the midst of a period of unprecedented advance in our understanding of the nervous system. As a result, a basic knowledge of neuroscience is fast becoming a requirement for students not only throughout the biological sciences but in some physical science and social science fields as well. Traditionally, neuroanatomy, one of the cornerstones of neuroscience, has been taught as a part of the medical school curriculum and has focussed on the structure of the human brain. However, for students in various fields of experimental neuroscience, human brains are not always readily available and are, in any case, of only secondary importance since experimental work must, of necessity, be carried out largely in animals. The sheep brain appears to be a good choice for study in student laboratories. It is large enough to be easily dissected and is readily available at low cost from biological supply houses. Consequently we have prepared a series of photographs of the sheep brain for use in student laboratories in neuroscience fields. In addition, appendices contain photographs of rat, cat, and monkey brains; photomicrographs of selected parts of the nervous system and of sense organs; and a series of schematic diagrams illustrating important brain circuits.

London, Ontario   C.H.V. & R.K.C.
June 1990

Methods

To prepare figures of the whole sheep brain for this book, an old ewe, purchased locally, was deeply anesthetized and perfused through the heart with a solution of formalin and sodium chloride. The brain was extracted from the skull and the meninges were removed, taking great care to avoid damage and to preserve the stumps of the cranial nerves. A parasagittal view of the whole sheep head was prepared by freezing and sawing in half a lamb's head which had been purchased from a butcher. Cross sections and dissections for the other figures were prepared from brains obtained from a biological supply house. Photographs of the whole brain and gross dissections were prepared using a view camera and sheet film (10.2 x 12.7 cm). Photographs of the cross sections of the sheep brain were prepared from frozen sections (cut with a microtome, 70 μ in thickness) which were placed on a glass slide, moistened with a few drops of 1.0% gelatin solution and used as "negatives" in a photographic enlarger. The photomicrographs were prepared using commercially prepared slides.

Suggested aids to study. The sheep brains which are ordinarily made available in student laboratories are free of surrounding skull, dura mater and major blood vessels. The first step in studying such a brain consists in the removal of the remaining meninges. The pituitary gland, if present, should be carefully freed from the surrounding tissue. The pia and arachnoid membranes and small blood vessels should be removed using a sharp forceps and fine scissors. Great care must be taken in removing these membranes from around the roots of the cranial nerves. The nerves pull out easily. In addition to providing a cleaned brain in which details can be easily observed, these procedures appear to facilitate learning. In order to clean the pia and arachnoid from a structure one must observe it very closely.

The brain should be bisected when a reasonable degree of familiarity with its superficial aspects has been acheived. To do this, place the brain on a table, dorsal surface up, and place the edge of a long thin knife in the medial longitudinal fissure. Cut through the midline of the brain in a single stroke.

Dissections from half or whole brains should be prepared with the assistance of a thin round-pointed spatula (about 1 cm wide) made from a soft wood (a popsicle stick will do). For example, such an instrument can be used to scrape away the grey matter of the neocortex, revealing the fibrous ridges (corona radiata) which lie in the base of the cortical gyri. Additional removal of the striatal grey in a half brain will reveal the fibres of the internal capsule (page 26). A book by Gluhbegovic and Williams (1980) shows what can be achieved by patient gross dissection.

To expose the hippocampal formation, the lateral ventricle should be opened and the overlying cortex removed (page 23). Large blocks of tissue can be cut away with a scalpel. Subsequently, the ventral tip of the hippocampal formation can be raised to expose the dorsal surface of the brainstem (page 24). Careful dissection of the tissue rostral to the ventral tip of the hippocampus will reveal the amygdala and an associated tract, the stria terminalis.

Horizontal or coronal sections of the brain can be prepared by making a series of cuts as suggested on page 28. In making coronal sections, it is easiest to judge the appropriate level for a cut if the brain is held with the ventral surface up. However, it is difficult to ensure that the plane of the cuts will correspond exactly to the plane of the sections shown in the photographs. The level of detail visible on the surface of thick blocks of tissue may

be somewhat disappointing in comparison to the thin
sections shown in pages 29-40. However, if the cut
surfaces are fresh and kept moist, a good deal can be seen.

Terminology

The terms chosen to designate brain structures in the
sheep are generally consistent with the usage of Kappers,
Huber, and Crosby (1936), Igarishi and Kamiya (1972)
and Yoshikawa (1968). Landacre (1930) has provided a
clear description of the sulci of the cerebral cortex of the
sheep. A stereotaxic atlas of the sheep brain is also
available (Richard, 1967). The terms used to refer to the cat
and rhesus monkey brains were adopted from Papez (1929)
and Hines (1933), respectively. An excellent general
introduction to the rat brain is provided by Zeman and Innes
(1963) and a comprehensive introduction to the scientific
neuroanatomical literature is provided by Brodal (1981).

References

Adrian, E.D. (1943). Afferent areas in the brain of
ungulates. Brain 66: 89-103.

Anthony, R., and De Grzybowski, J. (1936). Le neopallium
du mouton-étude de son developpement et
interpretation de ses plissements. J. Anat. 71: 41-53.

Bagley, C.Jr. (1922). Cortical motor mechanism of the
sheep brain. Arch. Neurol. Psychiat. 7: 417-453.

Brodal, A. (1981) Neurological anatomy in relation to
clinical medicine. New York: Oxford University Press
3 rd edition.

Cabral, R.J., and Johnson, J.I. (1971). The organization of
mechanoreceptive projections in the ventrobasal
thalamus of sheep. J. comp. Neurol. 141: 17-36.

Gluhbegovic, N., and Williams, T.H. (1980). The human
brain: A photographic guide. Hagerstown, Maryland:
Harper & Row.

Hines, M. (1933). The external morphology of the brain
and the spinal cord. In: C.G. Hartman and W.L. Strauss
(Eds.), The anatomy of the rhesus monkey (*Macaca
mulatta*). New York: Hafner Publishing Co.,
pp. 275-289.

Igarishi, S., and Kamiya, T. (1972). Atlas of the
vertebrate brain. Baltimore: University Park Press.

Kappers, C.U.A., Huber, G.C., and Crosby, E.C. (1936). The comparative anatomy of the nervous system of vertebrates, including man. New York: Hafner Publishing Co. (published as two volumes in 1936; reprinted as three volumes in 1965).

Landacre, F.L. (1930). The major and minor sulci of the brain of the sheep. Ohio J. Sci., 30: 36-51.

Papez, J.W. (1929). Comparative neurology: A manual and text for the study of the nervous system of vertebrates. New York: Hafner Publishing Co.

Richard, P. (1967). Atlas stéréotaxique du cerveau de brebis "Prealpes du Sud". Paris: Institut National de la Recherche Agronomique.

Simpson, S., and King, J.L. (1911). Localization of the motor area in the sheep. Quart. J exp. Physiol. 4: 53-65.

Woolsey, C.N., and Fairman, D. (1946). Contralateral, ipsilateral, and bilateral representation of cutaneous receptors in somatic areas I and II of the cerebral cortex of pig, sheep and other mammals. Surgery 19: 684-702.

Woudenberg, R.A. (1970). Projections of mechanoreceptive fields to cuneate-gracile and spinal trigeminal nuclear regions in sheep. Brain Research 17: 417-437.

Yoshikawa, T. (1968). Atlas of the brains of domestic animals. Tokyo: University of Tokyo Press.

Zeman, W., and Innes, J.R.M. (1963). Craigie's neuroanatomy of the rat. New York: Academic Press.

Whole Brain and Gross Dissections

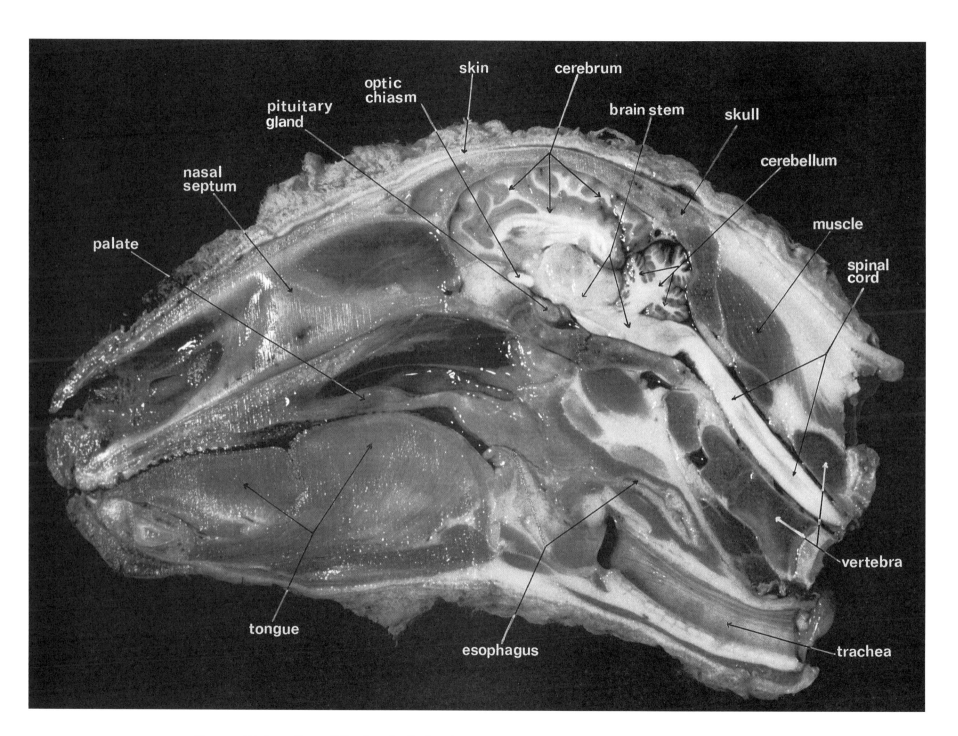

Parasagittal section of the head of a lamb

15

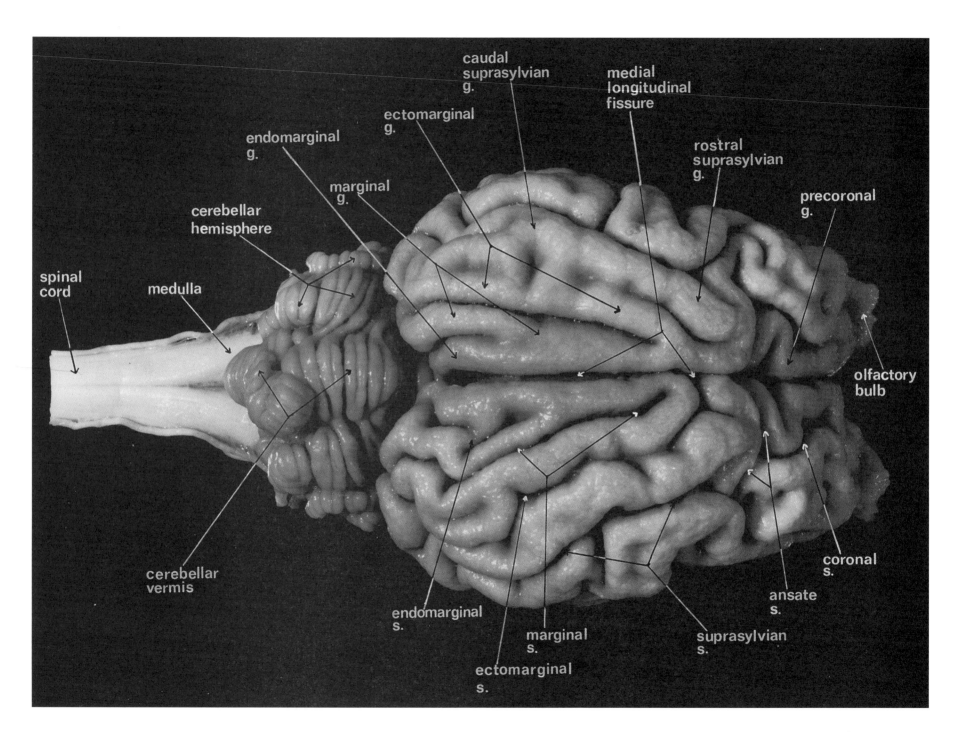

caudal
suprasylvian
g.

ectomarginal
g.

medial
longitudinal
fissure

endomarginal
g.

rostral
suprasylvian
g.

marginal
g.

precoronal
g.

cerebellar
hemisphere

spinal
cord

medulla

olfactory
bulb

cerebellar
vermis

endomarginal
s.

marginal
s.

ectomarginal
s.

suprasylvian
s.

ansate
s.

coronal
s.

Dorsal view of the sheep brain

16

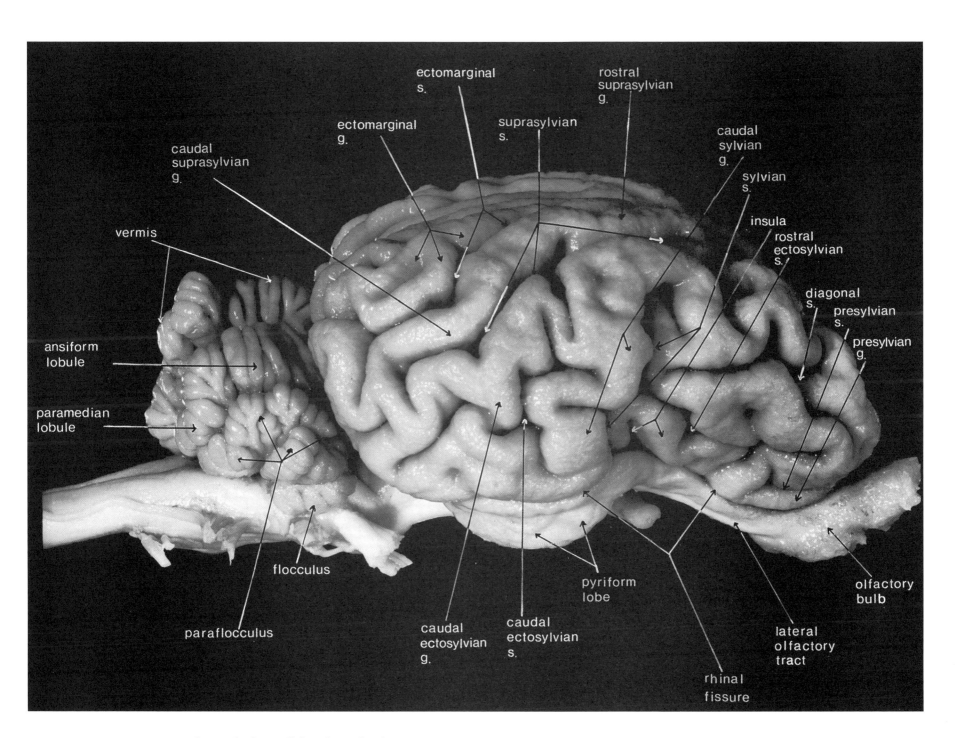

ectomarginal
s.

rostral
suprasylvian
g.

ectomarginal
g.

suprasylvian
s.

caudal
sylvian
g.

sylvian
s.

caudal
suprasylvian
g.

insula

rostral
ectosylvian
s.

vermis

diagonal
s.

presylvian
s.

ansiform
lobule

presylvian
g.

paramedian
lobule

flocculus

paraflocculus

caudal
ectosylvian
g.

caudal
ectosylvian
s.

pyriform
lobe

olfactory
bulb

lateral
olfactory
tract

rhinal
fissure

Lateral view of the sheep brain

17

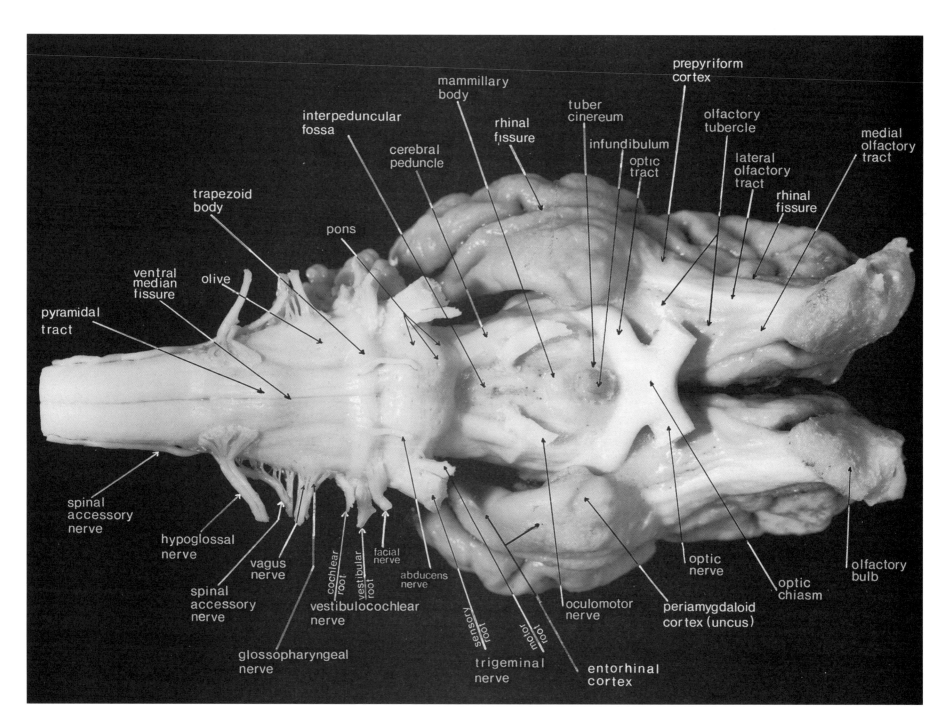

Ventral view of the sheep brain

18

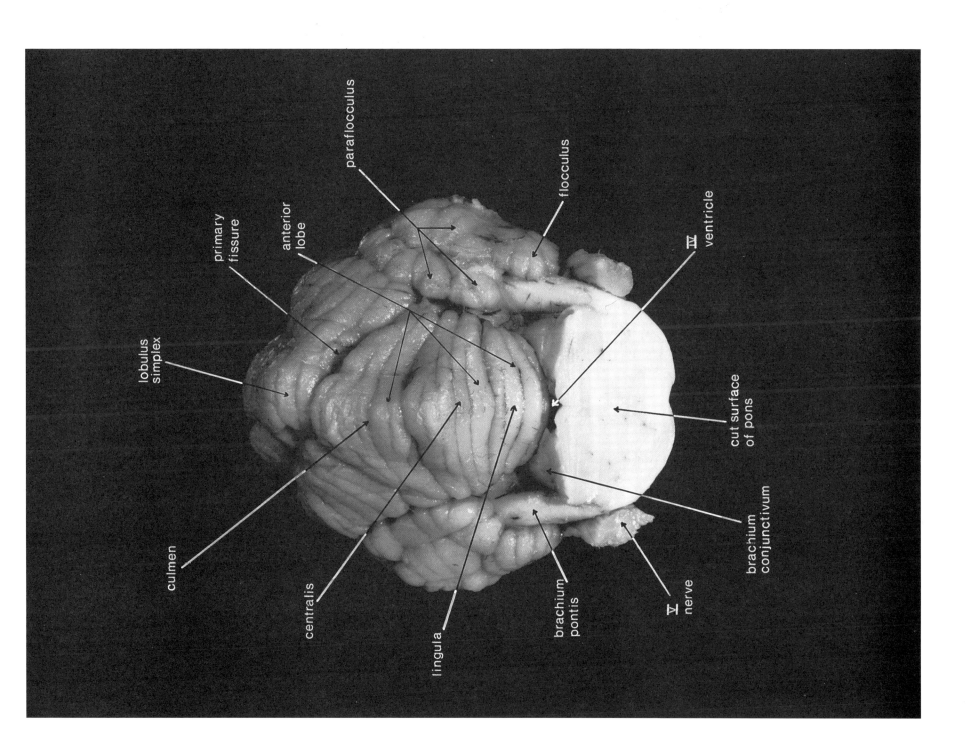

paraflocculus

flocculus

primary
fissure

anterior
lobe

IV
ventricle

lobulus
simplex

cut surface
of pons

culmen

brachium
conjunctivum

centralis

lingula

brachium
pontis

V
nerve

Rostral view of the cerebellum following section of the pons

19

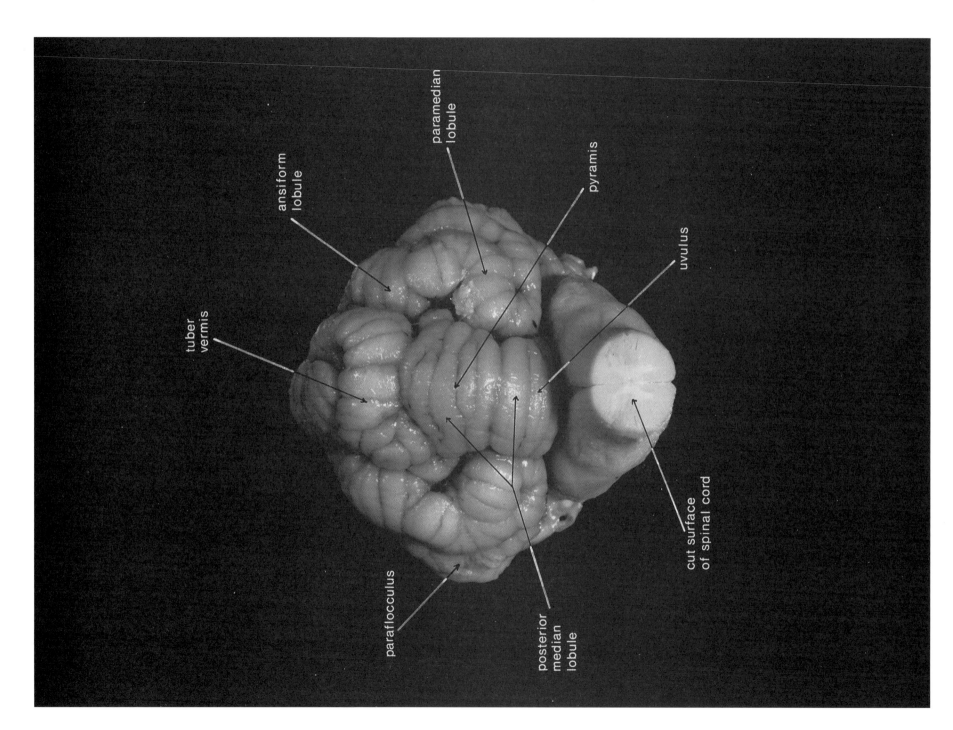

paramedian lobule

pyramis

ansiform lobule

uvulus

tuber vermis

cut surface of spinal cord

paraflocculus

posterior median lobule

Caudal view of the cerebellum

20

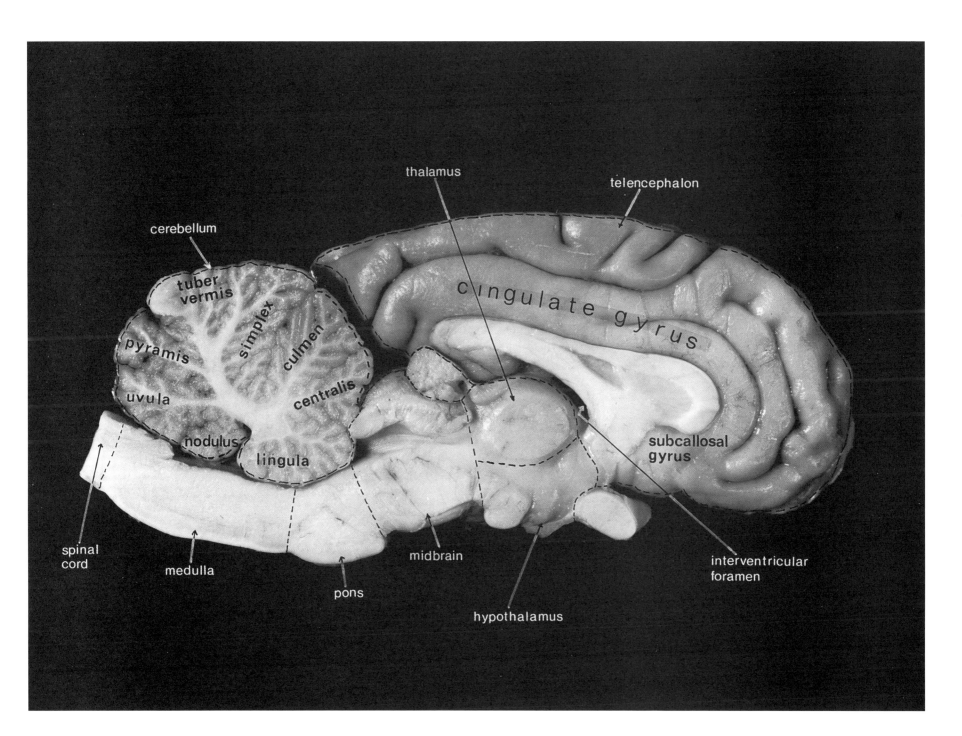

thalamus

telencephalon

cerebellum

tuber vermis

c i n g u l a t e   g y r u s

simplex

culmen

pyramis

uvula

centralis

subcallosal gyrus

nodulus

lingula

spinal cord

midbrain

interventricular foramen

medulla

pons

hypothalamus

Sagittal section of the sheep brain

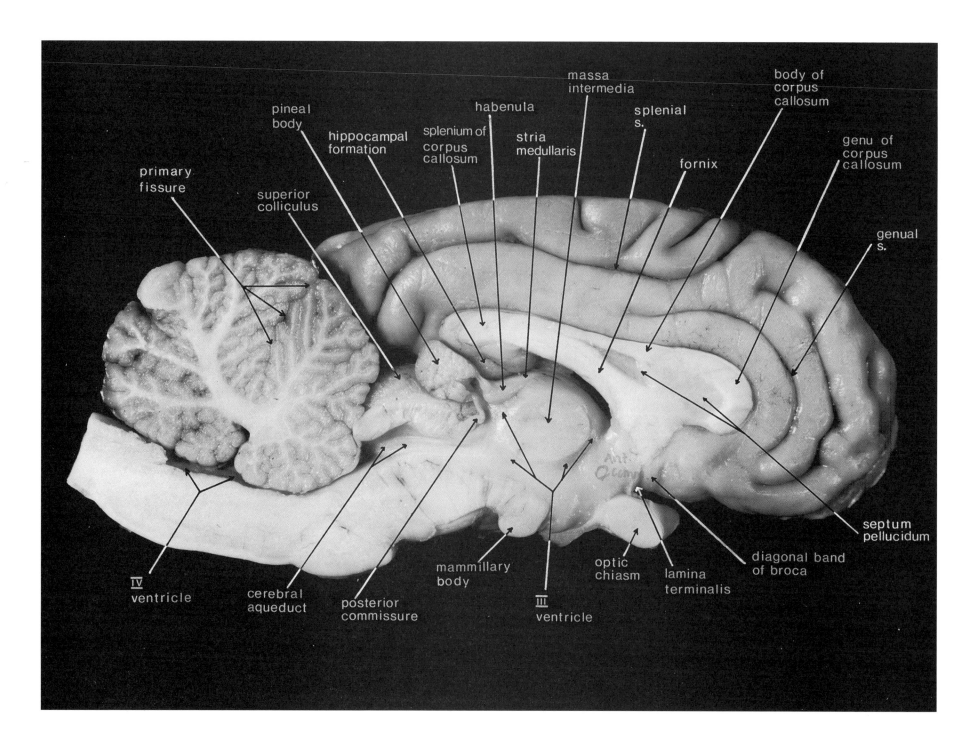

massa
intermedia

body of
corpus
callosum

pineal
body

habenula

splenial
s.

genu of
corpus
callosum

hippocampal
formation

splenium of
corpus
callosum

stria
medullaris

fornix

primary
fissure

superior
colliculus

genual
s.

septum
pellucidum

diagonal band
of broca

mammillary
body

optic
chiasm

lamina
terminalis

$\overline{IV}$
ventricle

cerebral
aqueduct

posterior
commissure

$\overline{III}$
ventricle

22   Sagittal section of the sheep brain showing additional details

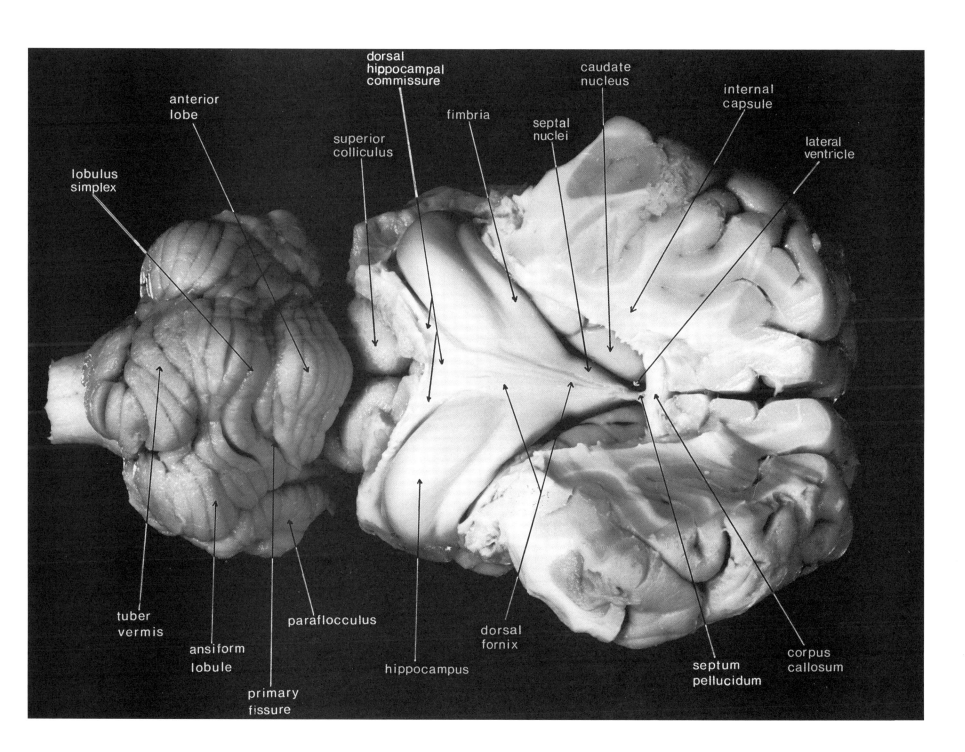

Dorsal view of the hippocampal formation and caudate nucleus   23

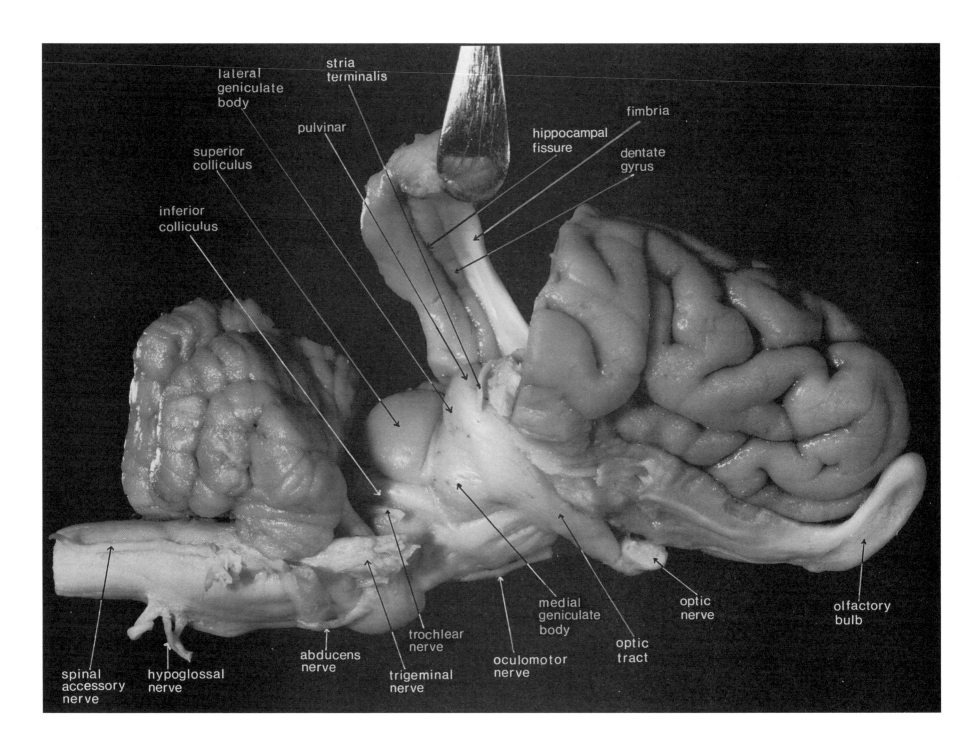

stria
terminalis

lateral
geniculate
body

pulvinar

fimbria

hippocampal
fissure

dentate
gyrus

superior
colliculus

inferior
colliculus

spinal
accessory
nerve

hypoglossal
nerve

abducens
nerve

trochlear
nerve

trigeminal
nerve

oculomotor
nerve

medial
geniculate
body

optic
tract

optic
nerve

olfactory
bulb

24   View of lateral brainstem and the medial hippocampal formation

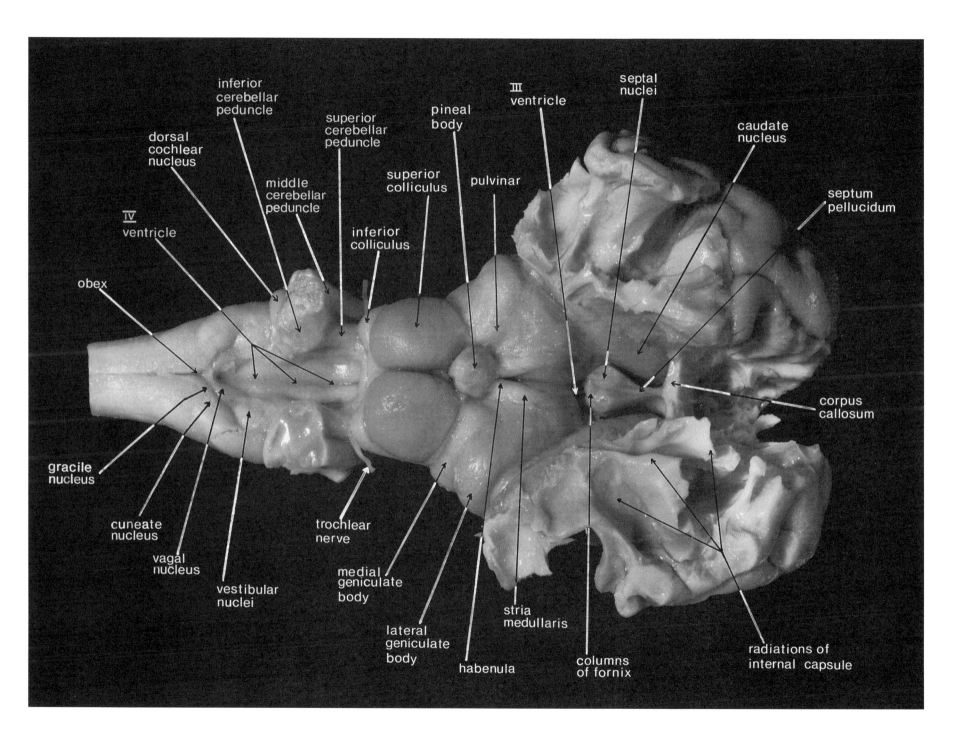

Dorsal view of the brainstem, diencephalon and striatum

25

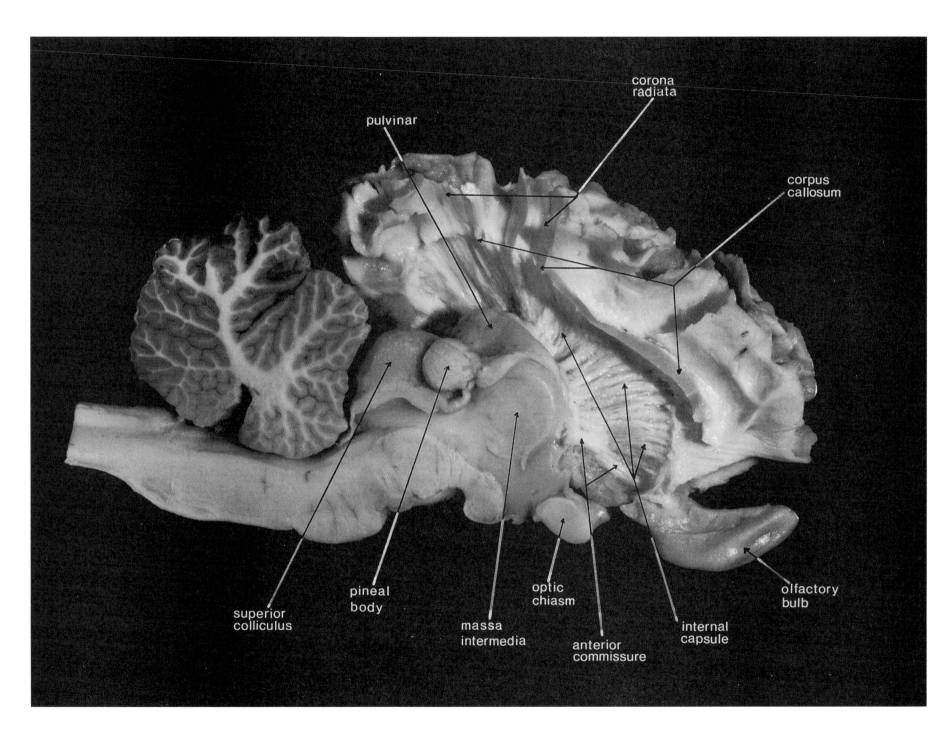

pulvinar

corona
radiata

corpus
callosum

superior
colliculus

pineal
body

massa
intermedia

optic
chiasm

anterior
commissure

internal
capsule

olfactory
bulb

Dissection showing the internal capsule and corona radiata

Cross Sections

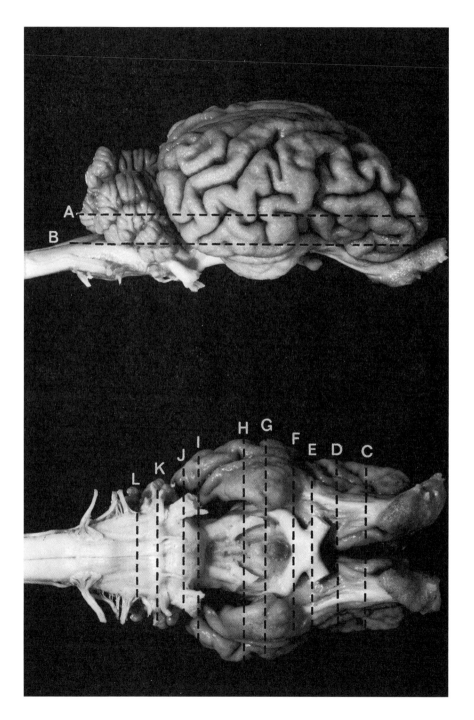

Cutting guide for preparing sections of the sheep brain

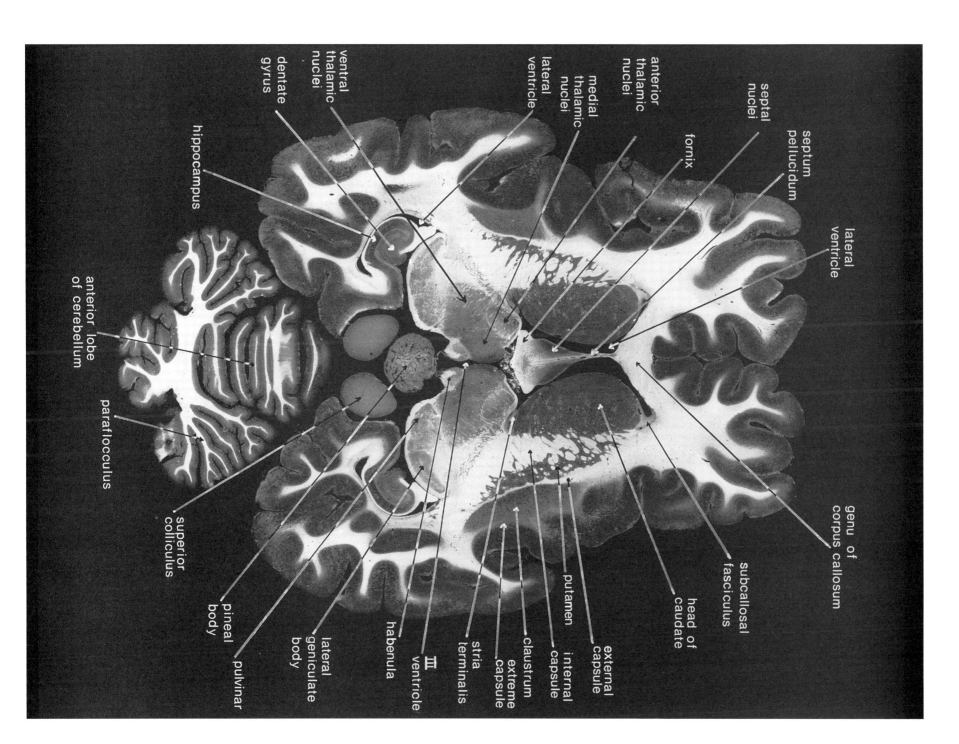

Level A. Horizontal section at the level of the pineal body

29

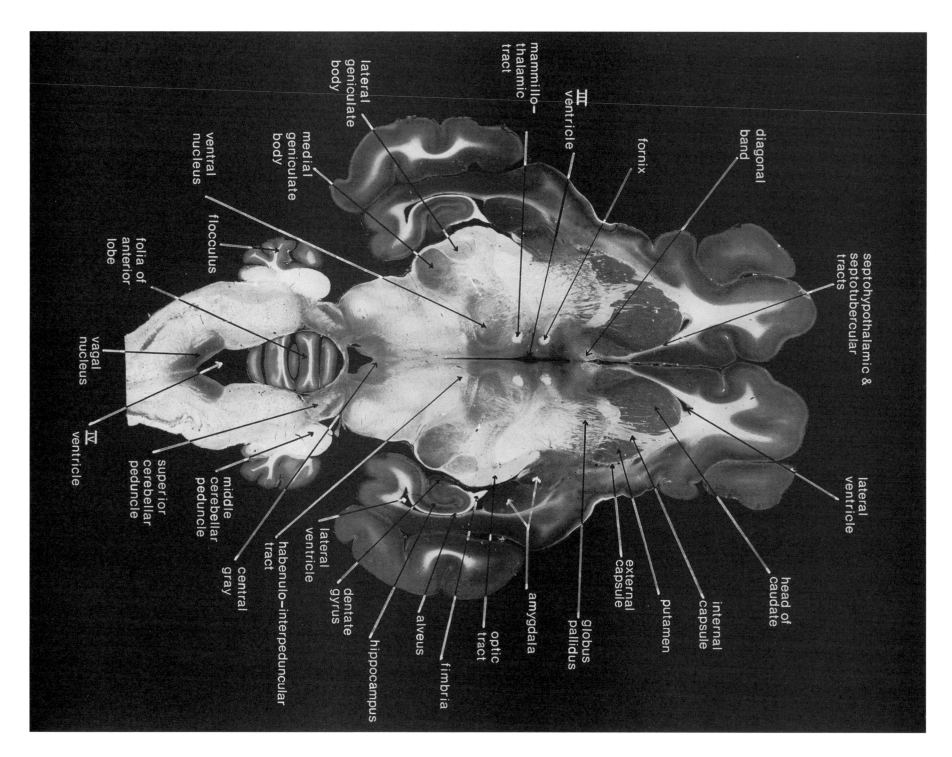

mammillo-
thalamic
tract

lateral
geniculate
body

medial
geniculate
body

ventral
nucleus

flocculus

folia of
anterior
lobe

vagal
nucleus

IV
ventricle

superior
cerebellar
peduncle

middle
cerebellar
peduncle

central
gray

habenulo-interpeduncular
tract

hippocampus

lateral
ventricle

dentate
gyrus

alveus

fimbria

optic
tract

amygdala

globus
pallidus

external
capsule

putamen

internal
capsule

head of
caudate

lateral
ventricle

septohypothalamic &
septotubercular
tracts

diagonal
band

fornix

III
ventricle

Level B. Horizontal section at a ventral level of the thalamus

30

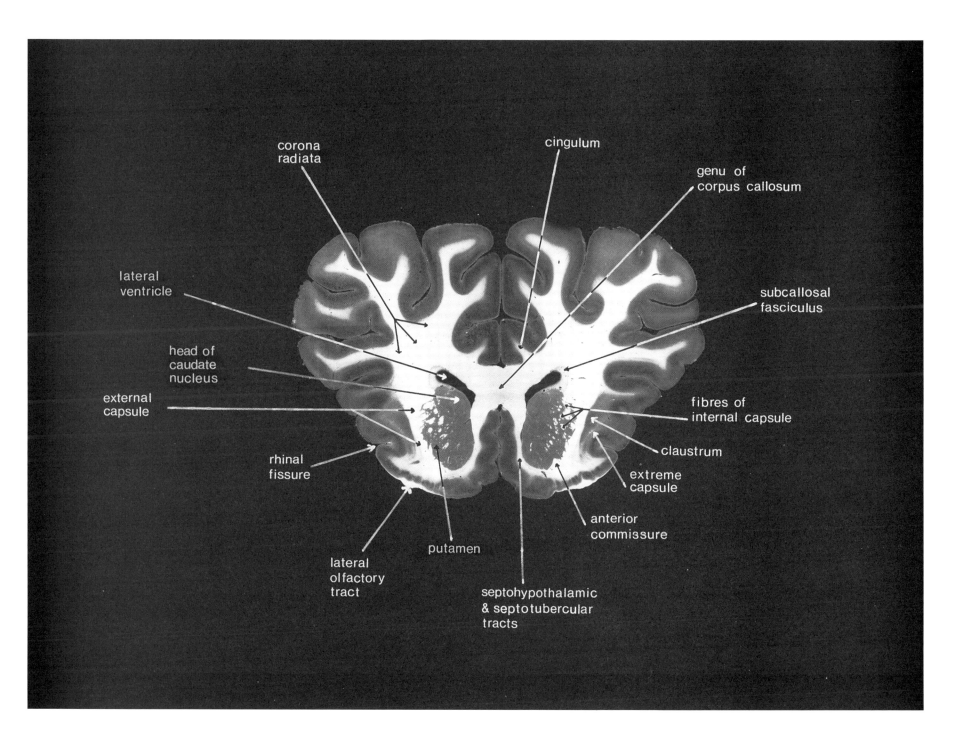

Level C. Coronal section caudal to the olfactory bulbs

31

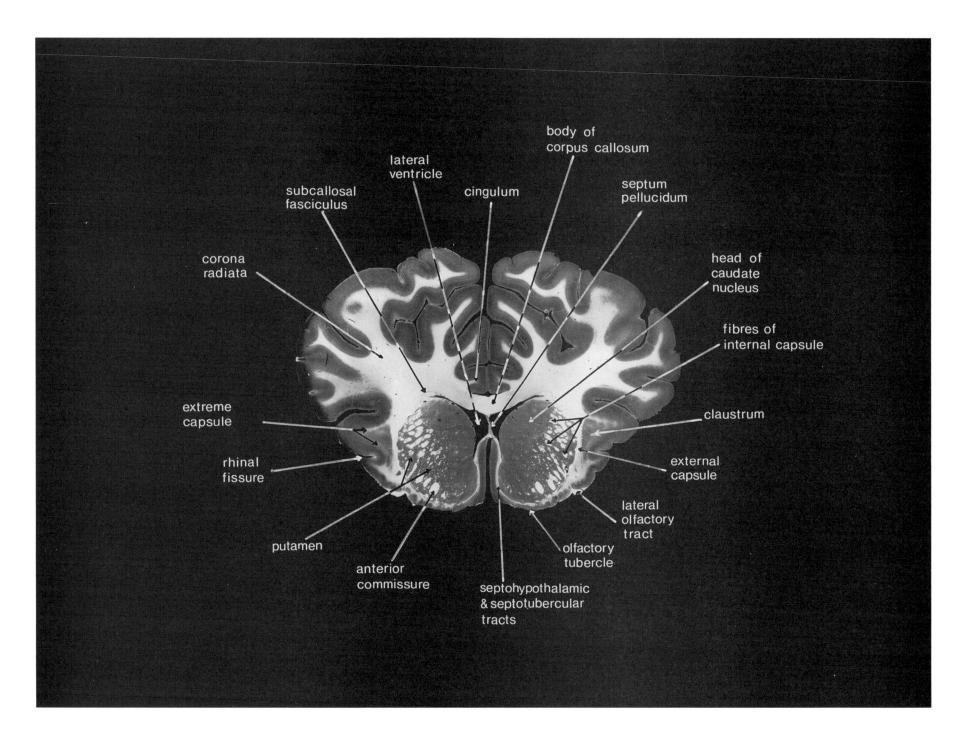

body of
corpus callosum

lateral
ventricle

subcallosal
fasciculus

cingulum

septum
pellucidum

corona
radiata

head of
caudate
nucleus

fibres of
internal capsule

extreme
capsule

claustrum

rhinal
fissure

external
capsule

putamen

lateral
olfactory
tract

anterior
commissure

olfactory
tubercle

septohypothalamic
& septotubercular
tracts

Level D. Coronal section through the olfactory tubercle

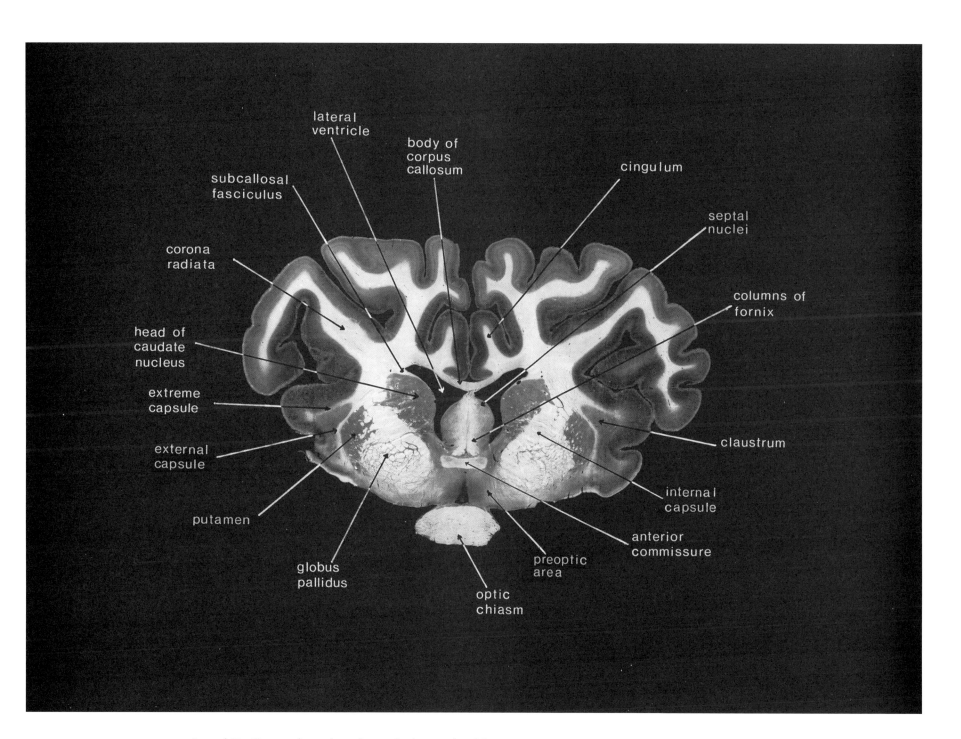

Level E. Coronal section through the optic chiasm

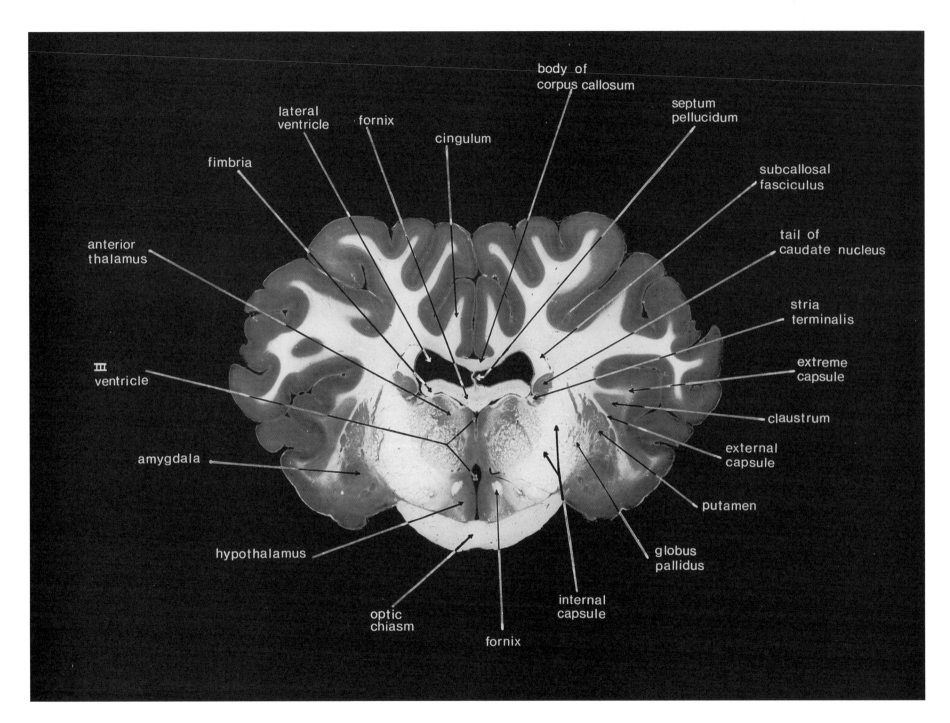

body of
corpus callosum

septum
pellucidum

lateral
ventricle

fornix

cingulum

subcallosal
fasciculus

fimbria

tail of
caudate nucleus

anterior
thalamus

stria
terminalis

extreme
capsule

III
ventricle

claustrum

external
capsule

amygdala

putamen

hypothalamus

globus
pallidus

optic
chiasm

internal
capsule

fornix

Level F. Coronal section near the caudal limit of the optic chiasm

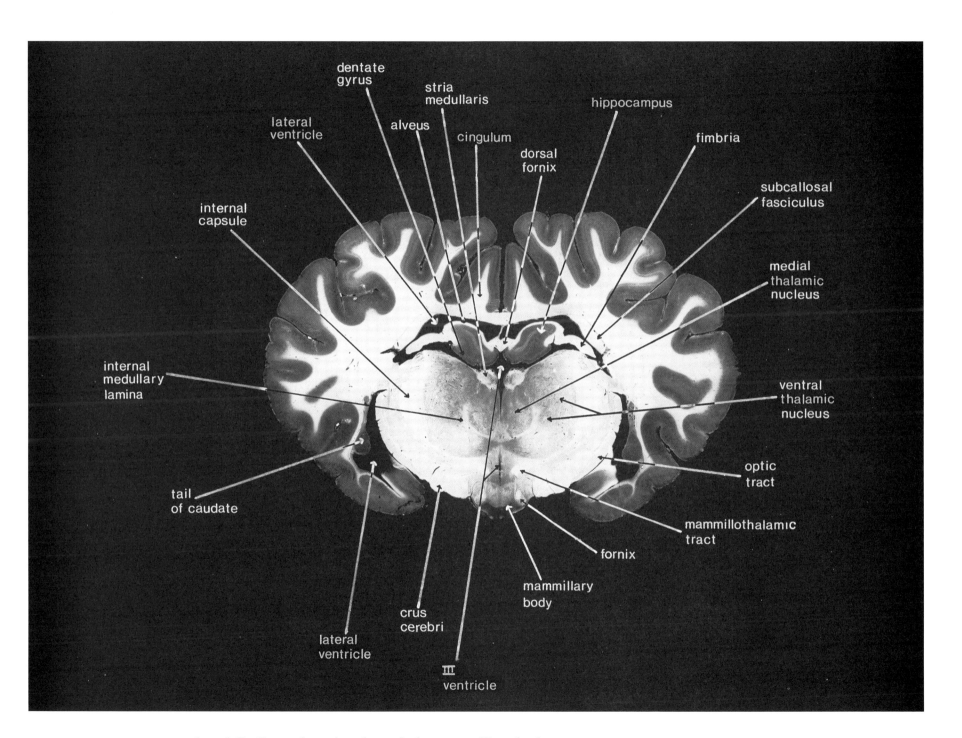

dentate
gyrus

stria
medullaris

hippocampus

lateral
ventricle

alveus

cingulum

fimbria

dorsal
fornix

subcallosal
fasciculus

internal
capsule

medial
thalamic
nucleus

internal
medullary
lamina

ventral
thalamic
nucleus

tail
of caudate

optic
tract

mammillothalamic
tract

fornix

lateral
ventricle

mammillary
body

crus
cerebri

III
ventricle

Level G. Coronal section through the mammillary body

35

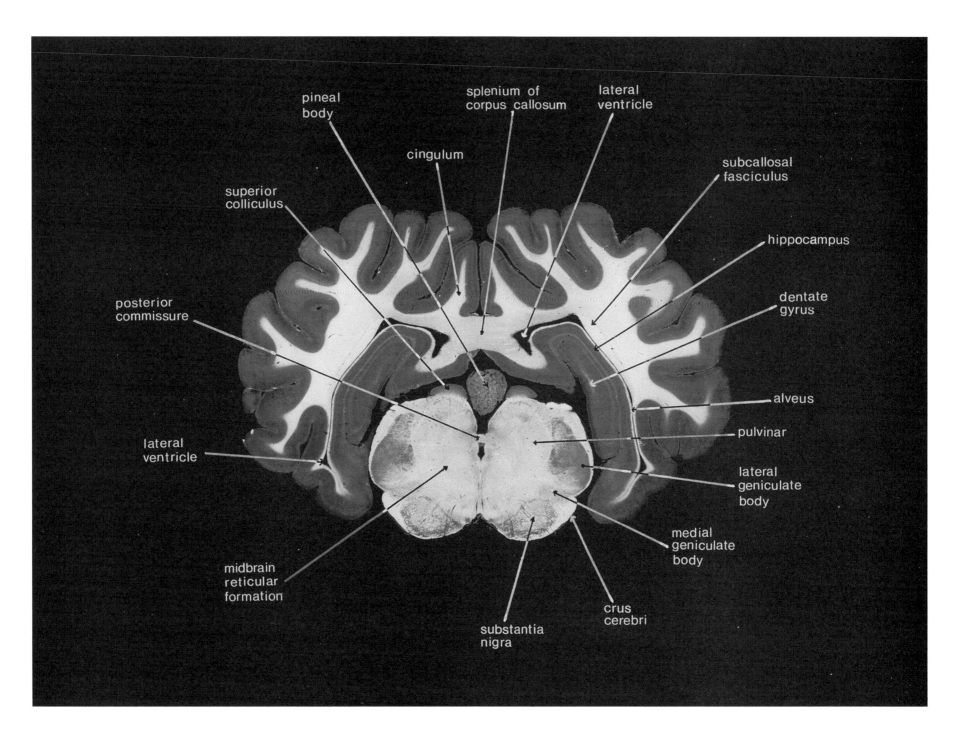

Level H. Coronal section through the cerebral peduncle

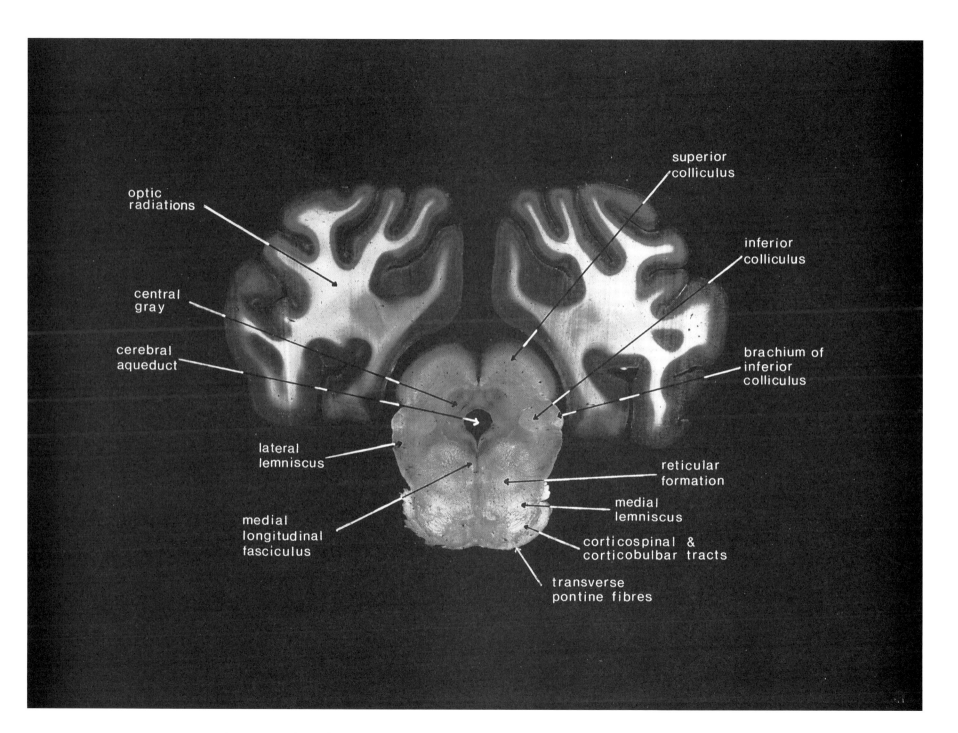

optic
radiations

superior
colliculus

inferior
colliculus

central
gray

cerebral
aqueduct

brachium of
inferior
colliculus

lateral
lemniscus

reticular
formation

medial
lemniscus

medial
longitudinal
fasciculus

corticospinal &
corticobulbar tracts

transverse
pontine fibres

Level I. Coronal section through the rostral pons

37

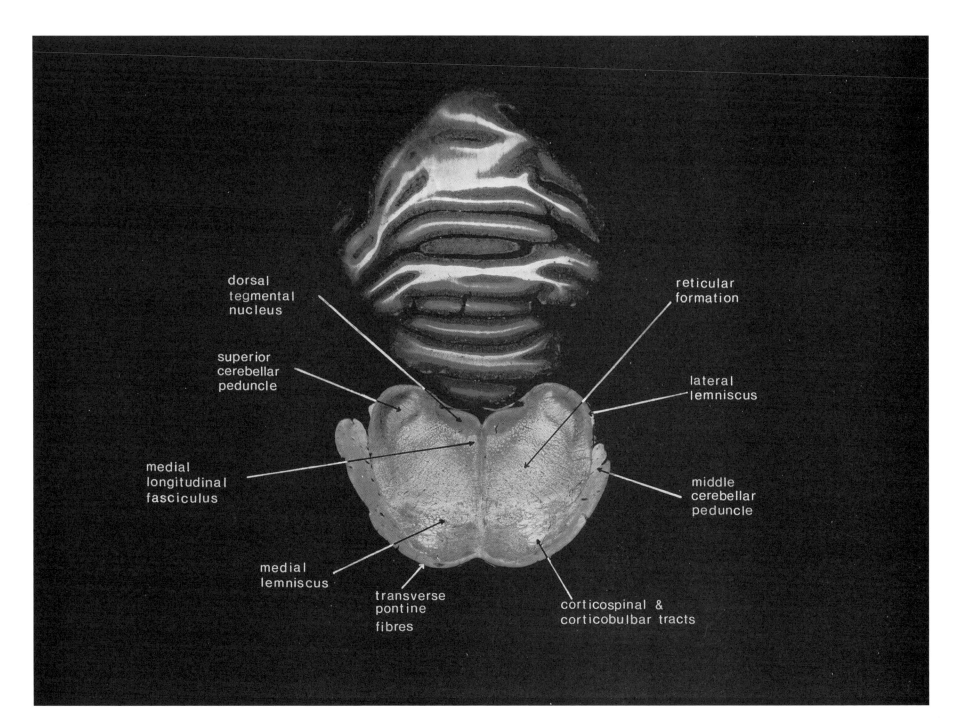

dorsal
tegmental
nucleus

reticular
formation

superior
cerebellar
peduncle

lateral
lemniscus

medial
longitudinal
fasciculus

middle
cerebellar
peduncle

medial
lemniscus

transverse
pontine
fibres

corticospinal &
corticobulbar tracts

Level J. Coronal section through the middle of the pons

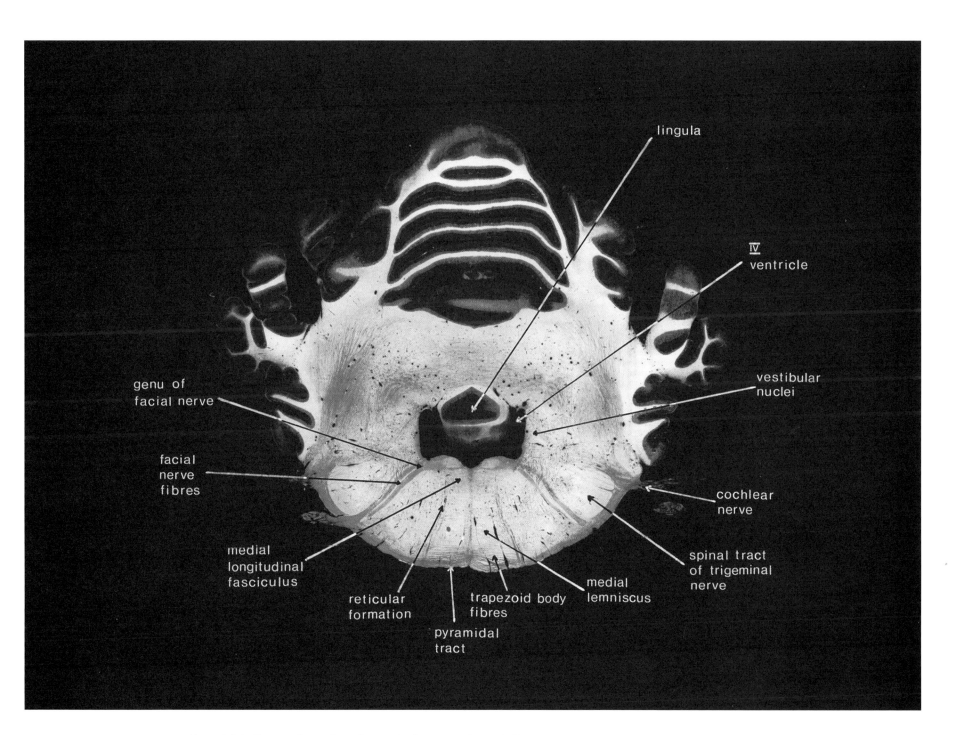

lingula

IV
ventricle

genu of
facial nerve

vestibular
nuclei

facial
nerve
fibres

cochlear
nerve

medial
longitudinal
fasciculus

spinal tract
of trigeminal
nerve

reticular
formation

trapezoid body
fibres

medial
lemniscus

pyramidal
tract

Level K. Coronal section through the rostral medulla

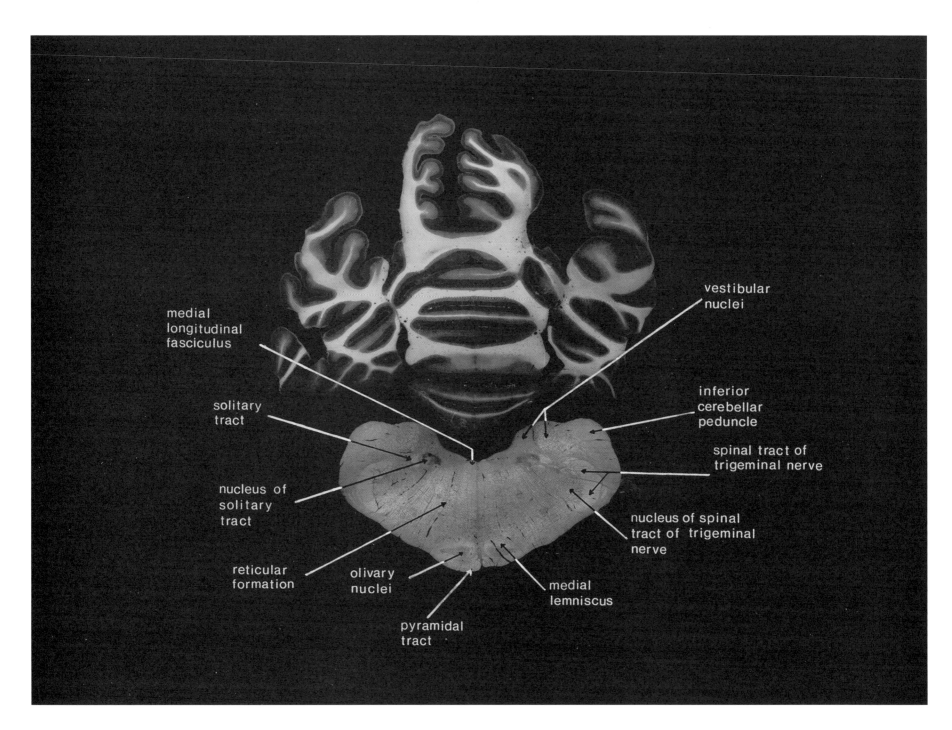

medial
longitudinal
fasciculus

vestibular
nuclei

solitary
tract

inferior
cerebellar
peduncle

spinal tract of
trigeminal nerve

nucleus of
solitary
tract

nucleus of spinal
tract of trigeminal
nerve

reticular
formation

olivary
nuclei

medial
lemniscus

pyramidal
tract

Level L. Coronal section just rostral to the glossopharyngeal nerve

Appendix I:
Brains of common laboratory
animals

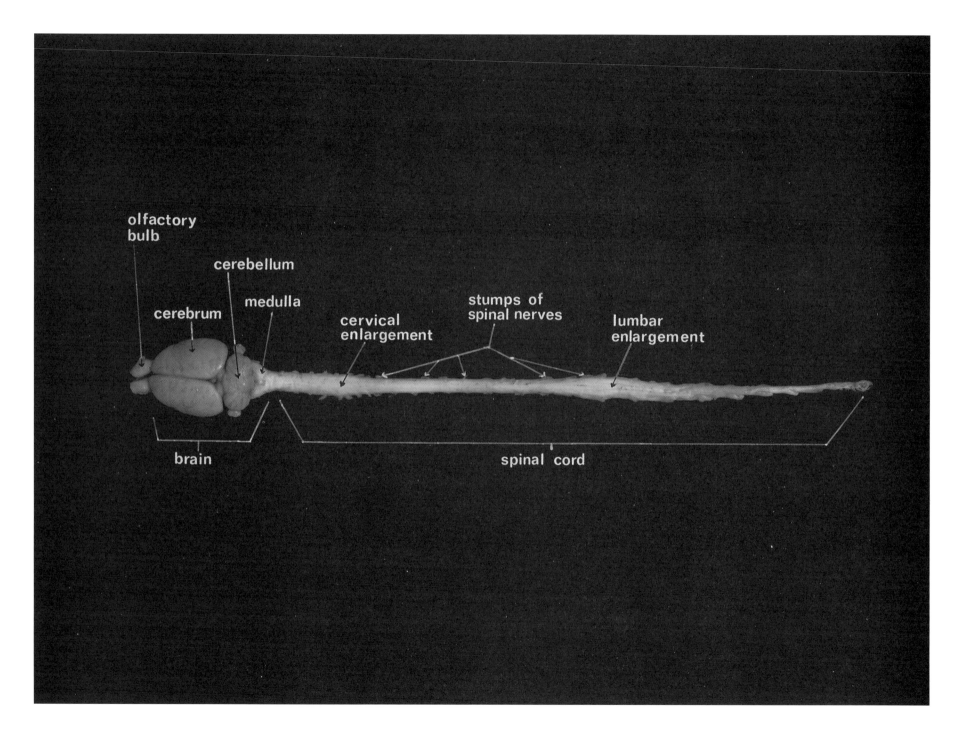

Dorsal view of the rat central nervous system

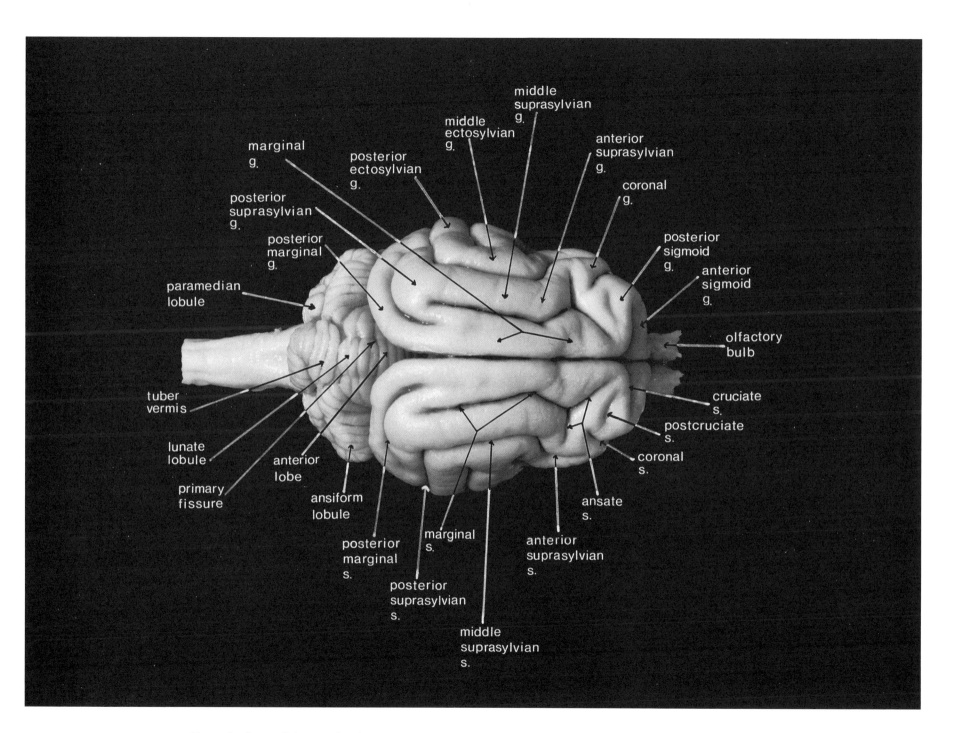

middle
suprasylvian
g.

middle
ectosylvian
g.

anterior
suprasylvian
g.

marginal
g.

posterior
ectosylvian
g.

coronal
g.

posterior
suprasylvian
g.

posterior
sigmoid
g.

posterior
marginal
g.

anterior
sigmoid
g.

paramedian
lobule

olfactory
bulb

cruciate
s.

tuber
vermis

postcruciate
s.

lunate
lobule

coronal
s.

anterior
lobe

primary
fissure

ansiform
lobule

ansate
s.

posterior
marginal
s.

marginal
s.

anterior
suprasylvian
s.

posterior
suprasylvian
s.

middle
suprasylvian
s.

Dorsal view of the cat brain

43

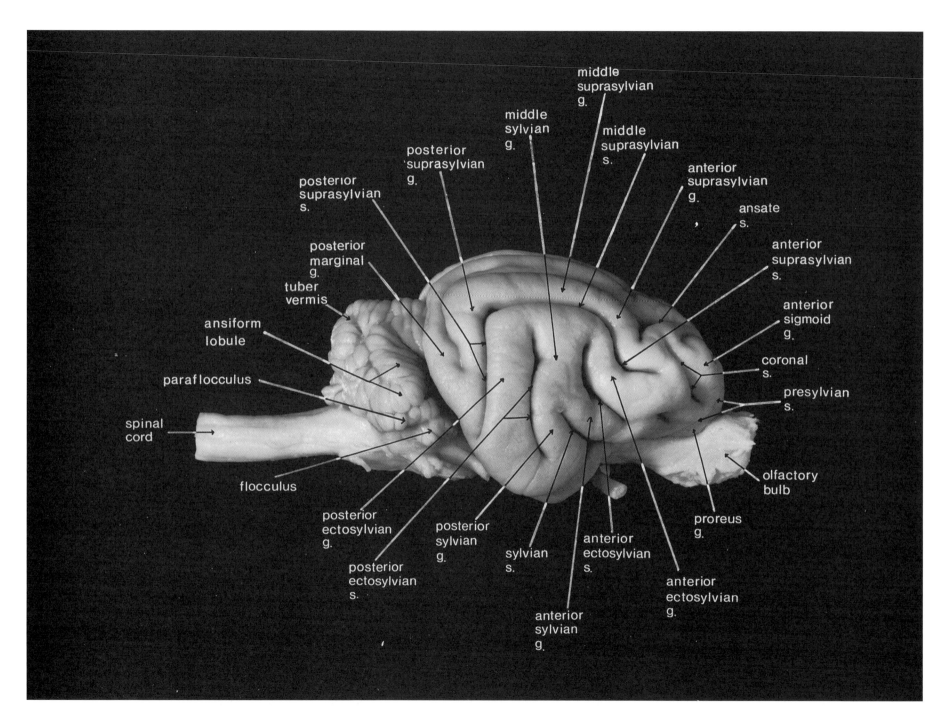

middle
suprasylvian
g.

middle
sylvian
g.

middle
suprasylvian
s.

posterior
suprasylvian
g.

anterior
suprasylvian
g.

posterior
suprasylvian
s.

ansate
s.

anterior
suprasylvian
s.

posterior
marginal
g.

anterior
sigmoid
g.

tuber
vermis

ansiform
lobule

coronal
s.

paraflocculus

presylvian
s.

spinal
cord

olfactory
bulb

flocculus

posterior
ectosylvian
g.

posterior
sylvian
g.

sylvian
s.

anterior
ectosylvian
s.

proreus
g.

posterior
ectosylvian
s.

anterior
ectosylvian
g.

anterior
sylvian
g.

Lateral view of the cat brain

44

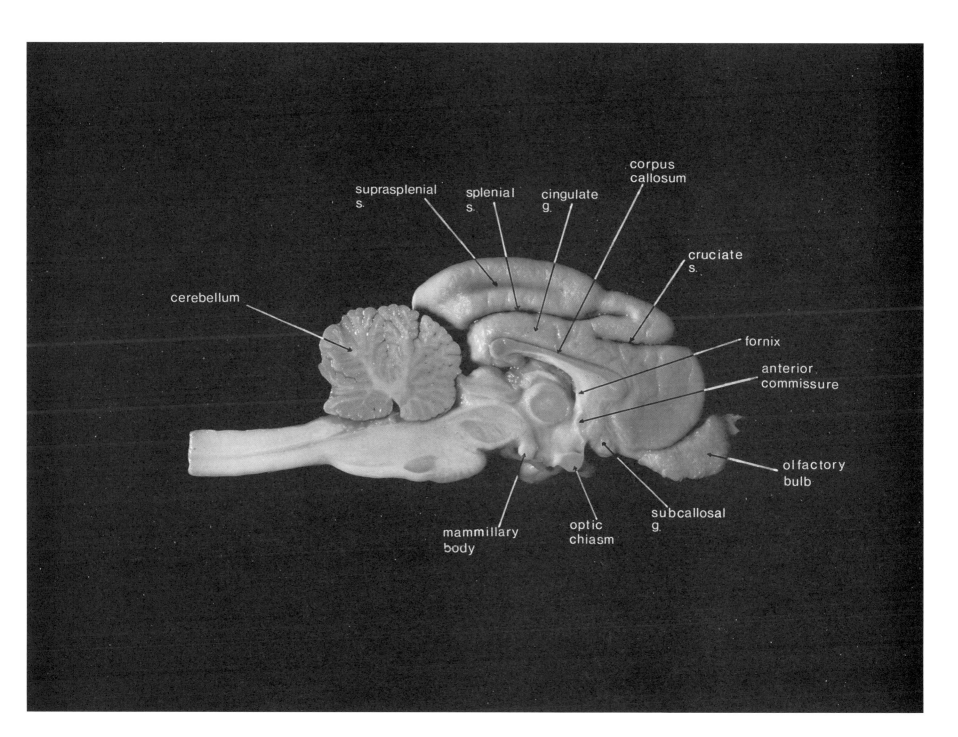

suprasplenial
s.

splenial
s.

cingulate
g.

corpus
callosum

cruciate
s.

cerebellum

fornix

anterior
commissure

olfactory
bulb

mammillary
body

optic
chiasm

subcallosal
g.

Sagittal section of the cat brain

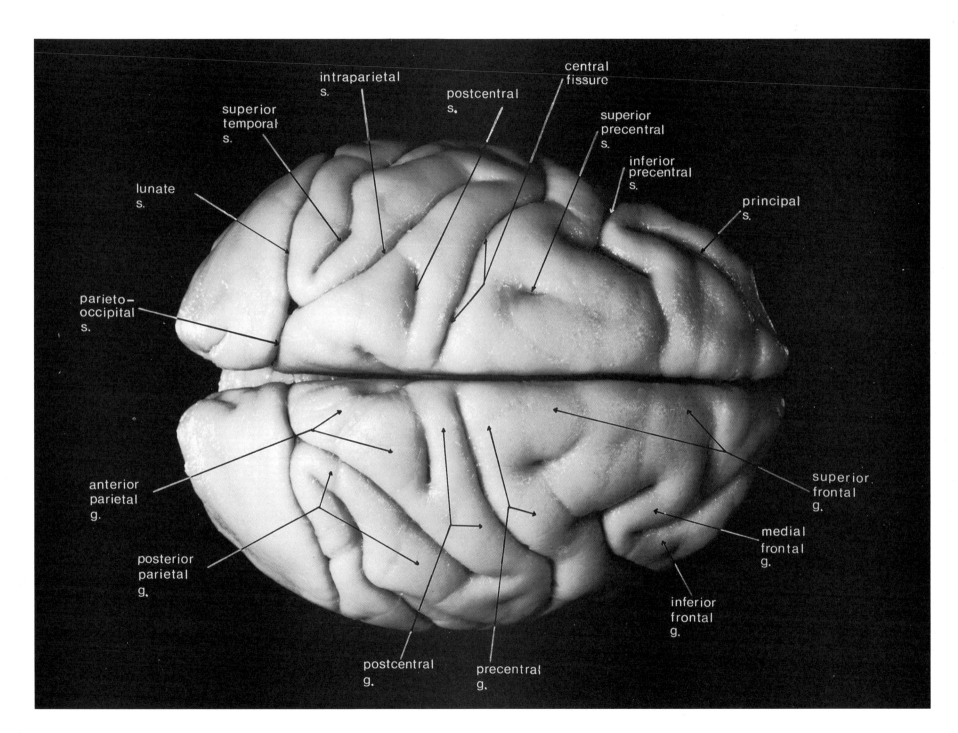

intraparietal s.

central fissure

superior temporal s.

postcentral s.

superior precentral s.

lunate s.

inferior precentral s.

principal s.

parieto-occipital s.

anterior parietal g.

superior frontal g.

posterior parietal g.

medial frontal g.

inferior frontal g.

postcentral g.

precentral g.

Dorsal view of rhesus monkey brain

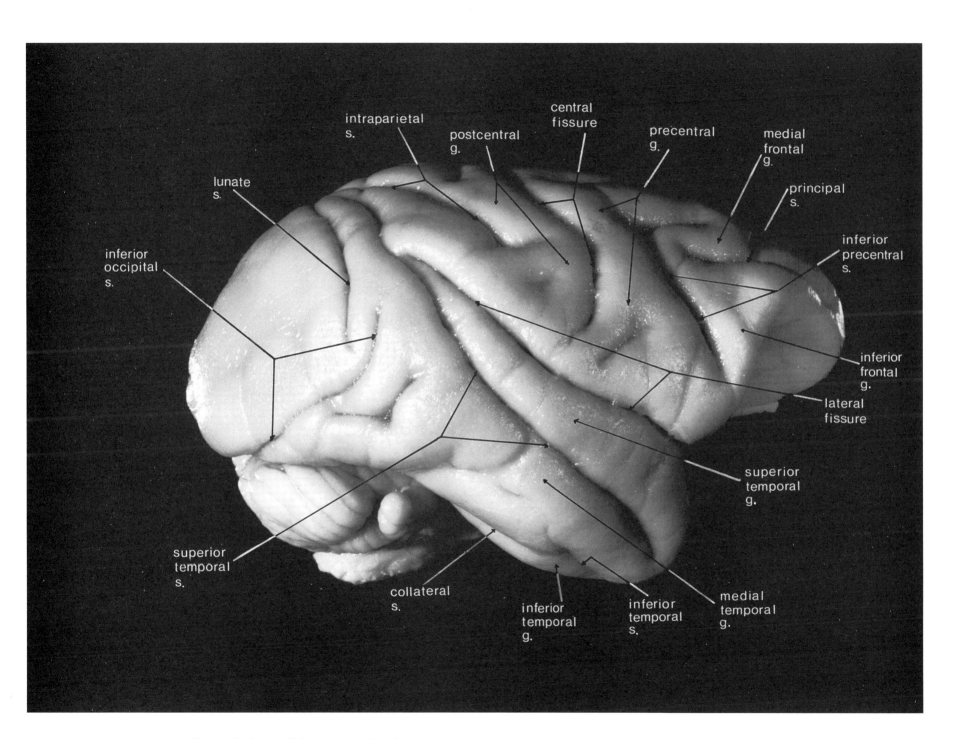

intraparietal s.

postcentral g.

central fissure

precentral g.

medial frontal g.

principal s.

lunate s.

inferior occipital s.

inferior precentral s.

inferior frontal g.

lateral fissure

superior temporal g.

superior temporal s.

collateral s.

inferior temporal g.

inferior temporal s.

medial temporal g.

Lateral view of rhesus monkey brain

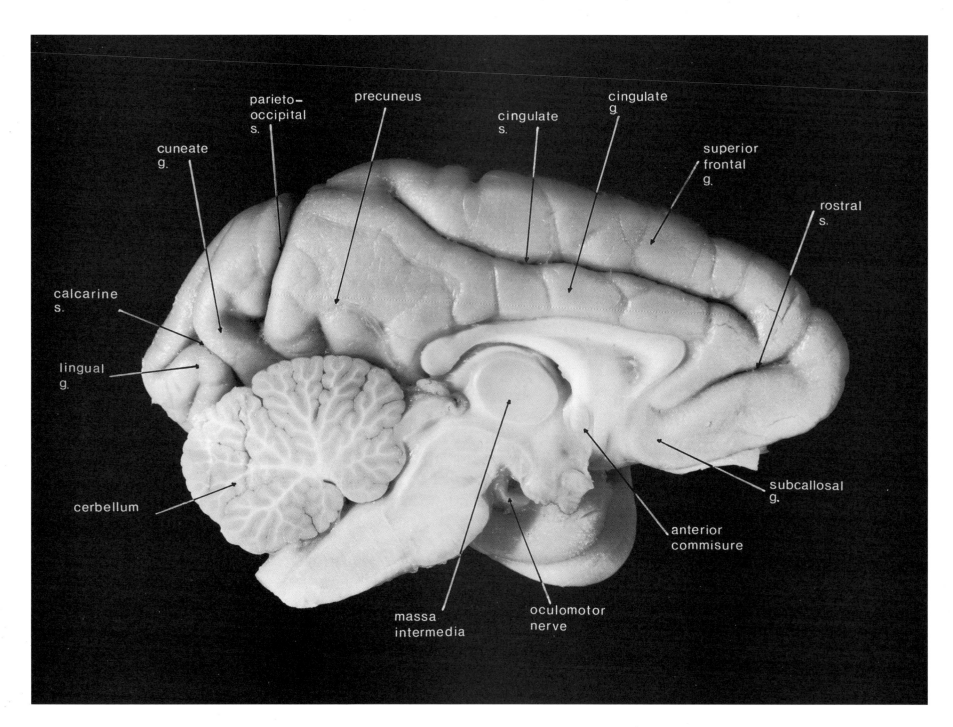

parieto-
occipital
s.

precuneus

cingulate
s.

cingulate
g.

superior
frontal
g.

cuneate
g.

rostral
s.

calcarine
s.

lingual
g.

subcallosal
g.

cerbellum

anterior
commisure

massa
intermedia

oculomotor
nerve

Sagittal section of rhesus monkey brain

Appendix II:
Microscopic structure of the
nervous system

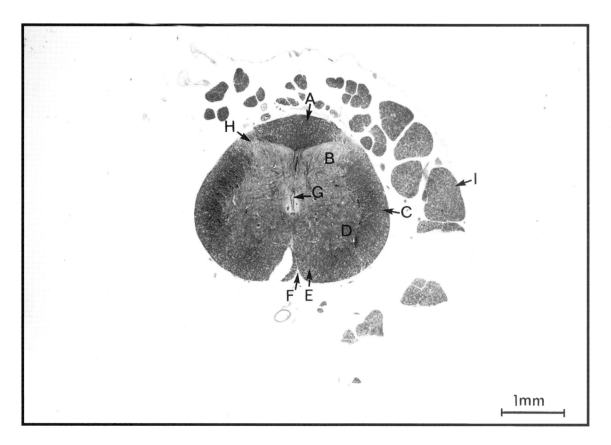

A:	dorsal column
B:	dorsal horn
C:	lateral column
D:	ventral horn
E:	ventral column
F:	ventral median fissure
G:	central canal
H:	Lissauer's tract
I:	cauda equina

1mm

Figure 1. Dog spinal cord, cross section, sacral level.

The spinal cord lies within the vertebral canal, surrounded by meninges (pia, arachnoid membrane, dura) and cerebrospinal fluid. It consists of a long, roughly cylindrical tube with a central lumen (the central canal) but is enlarged in the cervical and lumbar regions (see p. 42, Appendix I). At regular intervals, spinal nerves are connected to the cord by dorsal and ventral roots (see diagram in Figure 18, Appendix III). The dorsal roots contain afferent fibers that supply input to the dorsal and ventral horn cells in the cord and ascending fibers to the brain; the ventral roots contain mainly efferent fibers that arise from the motor neurones of the ventral horn. The two spinal roots combine to form a spinal nerve which leaves the vertebral canal between adjacent vertebrae. At its caudal extremity the spinal cord tapers to a point (the conus medullaris) surrounded by a brush of spinal nerves (the cauda equina).

The number of spinal nerves varies in different mammalian species. In man there are 8 cervical nerves, 12 thoracic nerves, 5 lumbar nerves, 5 sacral nerves and usually 1 coccygeal nerve, making a total of 31.

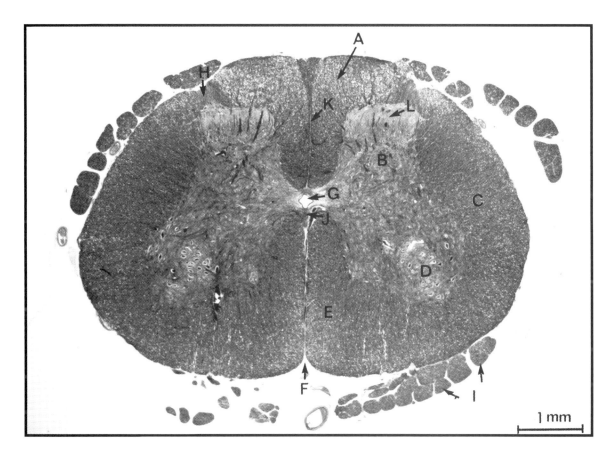

A: dorsal column
B: dorsal horn
C: lateral column
D: ventral horn
E: ventral column
F: ventral median
     fissure
G: central canal
H: Lissauer's tract
I: cauda equina
J: ventral white
     commissure
K: dorsal median
     septum
L: substantia
     gelatinosa

1 mm

Figure 2. Dog spinal cord, cross section, lumbar level.

Note that in the spinal cord the fiber tracts (the columns, or white matter) lie mainly on the outside of the structure while the cell bodies (the horns, or grey matter) cluster in a butterfly shaped structure in the interior. In contrast, in the brain the cell-rich cerebral and cerebellar cortices lie on the outside of the structure.

The lumbar enlargement and the rostral part of the sacral level of the spinal cord contain sensory, motor and internuncial neurons governing the hind limb; the cervical enlargement contains similar elements governing the forelimb, neck and diaphragm. The thoracic part of the cord, lying between the lumbar and cervical enlargements, provides sensory and motor innervation of the trunk. The sacral levels of the cord also innervate the pelvic viscera such as the sphincters, bladder and genitalia.

Note the large ventral horn cells (somatomotor neurons) in the ventral horn. The substantia gelatinosa is a subdivision of the dorsal horn.

51

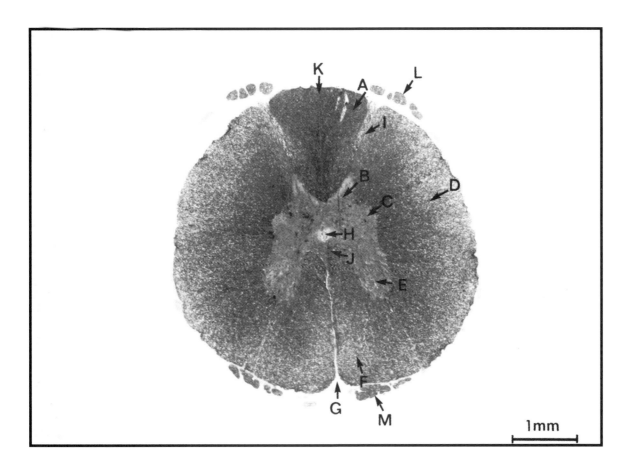

A:	dorsal column
B:	dorsal horn
C:	lateral horn
D:	lateral column
E:	ventral horn
F:	ventral column
G:	ventral median fissure
H:	central canal
I:	Lissauer's tract
J:	ventral white commissure
K:	dorsal median septum
L:	dorsal root fibers
M:	ventral root fibers

1mm

Figure 3.   Dog spinal cord, cross section, thoracic level.

Note that both dorsal and ventral horns in the thoracic cord are much smaller than in the lumbar and cervical parts of the cord. This is related to the relatively poor sensory discrimination in the trunk as compared to the limbs (e.g. the two-point threshold is much higher on the back than on the fingers or toes) and to the limited number of movements the trunk can make in comparison to the limbs. Note also the lateral horns, containing the cell bodies of preganglionic autonomic neurons which innervate visceral structures.

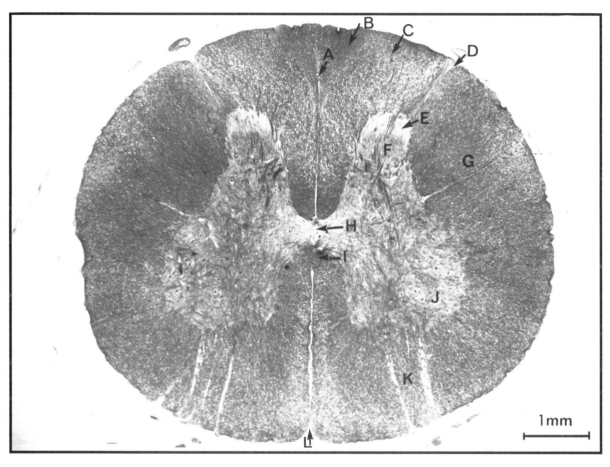

A:	dorsal median septum
B:	gracile fasciculus
C:	cuneate fasciculus
D:	Lissauer's tract
E:	substantia gelatinosa
F:	dorsal horn
G:	lateral column
H:	central canal
I:	ventral white commissure
J:	ventral horn
K:	ventral column
L:	ventral median fissure

Figure 4. Dog spinal cord, cross section, cervical level.

Over the series of 4 spinal levels, note that the columns (white matter) are largest at the cervical levels and tend to diminish as one progresses caudally. There are two main reasons for this. At a cervical level sensory afferents representing the entire body ascend to the brain but at more caudal spinal levels only the more caudal parts of the body are represented. Similarly at a cervical level, all descending motor fibers are present but at the thoracic and sacral spinal levels, motor fibers controlling the neck and forelimb are not present. Therefore, both ascending sensory and descending motor fibers are more numerous at rostral levels than at caudal levels of the spinal cord.

Note that the gracile and cuneate fasciculi together constitute the dorsal columns at the cervical level.

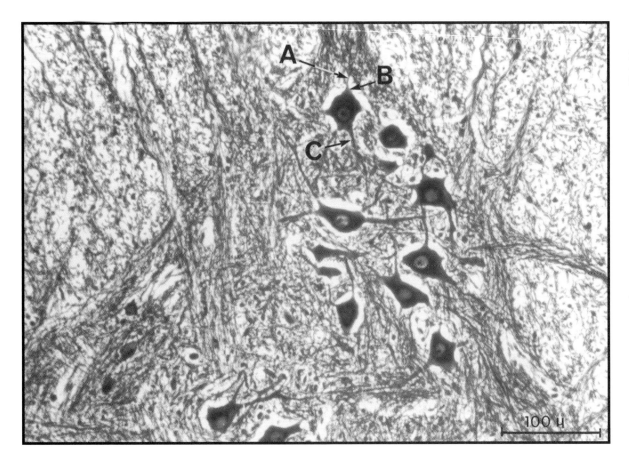

A: axon
B: axon hillock
C: dendrite

Figure 5. Ventral horn cells from monkey spinal cord. Silver stain.

Silver salts such as silver nitrate, though colorless in solution, are selectively precipitated over certain cell and tissue components. Note the cell bodies (somata or perikarya) and the dense network of fine dendritic or axonal processes (neuropil). These fine fibers are mostly unmyelinated. At high magnification, in silver stained material, it may be possible to distinguish neurofibrils running longitudinally within cell bodies or their processes. Note that the cell bodies contain a darkly stained nucleolus within a pale nucleus.

Large motoneurones that project to the muscle fibers whose contraction provides a large mechanical force (extra-fusal muscle fibers) are called alpha motoneurones. Smaller gamma motoneurones project to small muscle fibers contained within muscle spindles, a type of proprioceptor. The small intra-fusal muscle fibers contained within muscle spindles make no <u>direct</u> contribution to the mechanical force generated by a muscle.

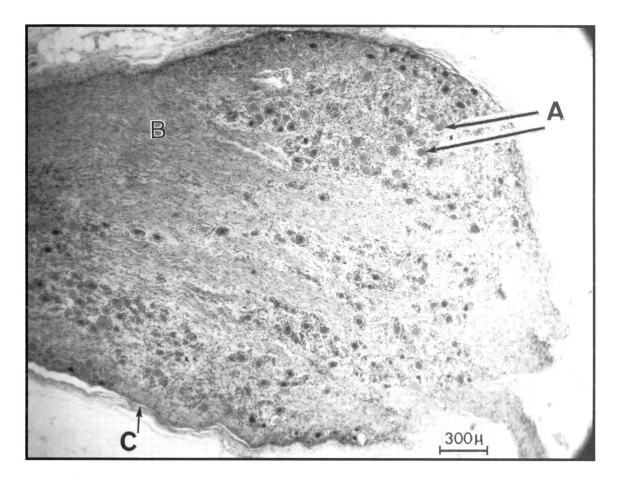

A: dorsal root
    ganglion cells
B: axons
C: capsule of
    ganglion

300μ

Figure 6. Spinal dorsal root ganglion.

All the cell bodies of spinal afferent neurons lie in ganglia outside, but close to, the spinal cord. A single process leaves these cell bodies and divides in a T shaped junction. One limb of the T enters the spinal cord while the other limb supplies the body wall or viscera. Both limbs function as axons, carrying sensory information from receptors, such as Pacinian corpuscles, to the spinal cord. Note that each cell soma is surrounded by smaller satellite cells. The bundles of axons (B) have a wavy or snake-like appearance, as they do in all peripheral nerves. This probably permits a nerve to be elongated to some extent, without injury. The capsule of the ganglion consists of connective tissue.

The larger fibers that enter the spinal cord via a dorsal root form the <u>medial division</u> of the root and enter the dorsal column. Finer, often unmyelinated, fibers enter via the <u>lateral division</u> of the dorsal root and run in Lissauer's tract.

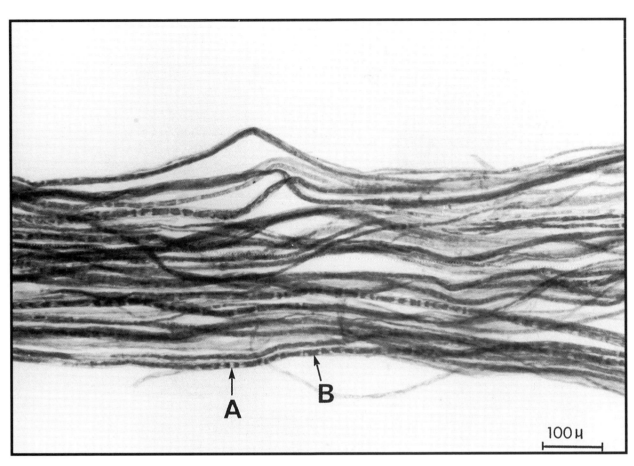

A: node of Ranvier
B: internode

100 μ

Figure 7. Fibers of peripheral nerve, teased apart. Myelin stain.

Note that myelin is arranged in short segments along the nerve fibers like beads on a string. The gaps between successive "beads" are the nodes of Ranvier and the "beads" are internodes. The myelin surrounding peripheral nerve fibers consists of the membranes of Schwann cells wrapped around each nerve fiber. In the central nervous system oligodendroglial cells perform a similar function.

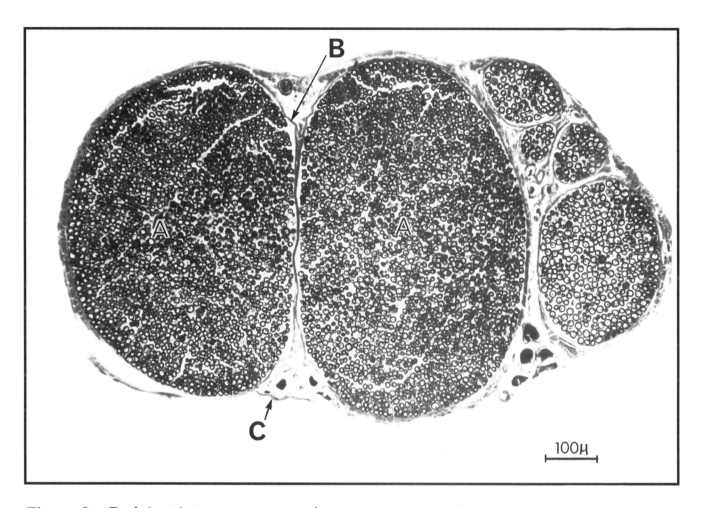

A: axons
B: perineurium
C: epineurium

Figure 8. Peripheral nerve, cross section. Myelin stain.

A peripheral nerve consists of large numbers of myelinated and unmyelinated (not visible here) axons bound together into fascicles by a tough connective tissue coat, the perineurim. Groups of fascicles may be bound together by a thinner coat, the epineurim. Within a fascicle, fine fibrils of endoneurium may be visible. Note that each axon consists of a myelin ring surrounding a nerve fiber.

The fibers are very much shrunken by the staining procedure. Normally, the myelin sheath and its enclosed nerve fiber are in close contact.

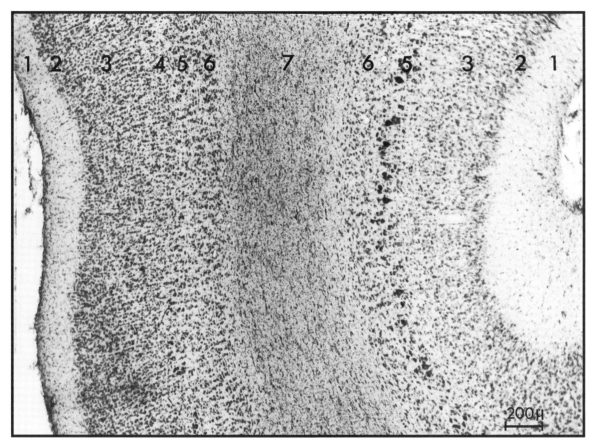

1: molecular layer
2: external granular layer
3: external pyramidal layer
4: internal granular layer
5: internal pyramidal layer
6: polymorphic or multiform cell layer

Layer 1 consists mainly of fine fibers, both dendrites and axons, which originate from neurons lying deeper in the cortex or in subcortical structures (only axons). Layers 2 and 4 contain large numbers of granule cells which are local circuit neurons with short axons. Layer 4 is the main cortical target of thalamocortical projection fibers which branch profusely in this zone. Note that layer 4 is largely missing in the sigmoid gyrus. Layers 3 and 5 contain pyramidal cells, larger neurons with longer axons and a long apical dendrite (see Figure 10). Cortical efferent projections to subcortical structures such as the pons or spinal cord generally originate from pyramidal cells in layer 5 while callosal projections to the opposite hemisphere arise from pyramidal cells in layers 3 and 5. In the sigmoid gyrus, layer 5 contains giant pyramidal cells (Betz cells). Modified pyramidal cells (often called spindle cells) in layer 6 are the origin of corticothalamic projection fibers. Thalamocortical projections are generally reciprocated by corticothalamic projections, e.g. the lateral geniculate nucleus projects to the striate cortex and the striate cortex projects to the lateral geniculate nucleus. Layer 7 is white matter containing axons afferent or efferent to the two areas of cortex.

Figure 9. Section showing two types of cortex in cat brain.

This preparation was made using a Nissl stain, which attaches itself to the Nissl substance (named after Franz Nissl, a German neurologist). Nissl substance consists mainly of ribonucleic acids in ribosomes associated with rough endoplasmic reticulum. The left part of the section shows the cell layers of the anterior ectosylvian gyrus. The right part of the section shows the sigmoid gyrus (area 4 of Brodmann).

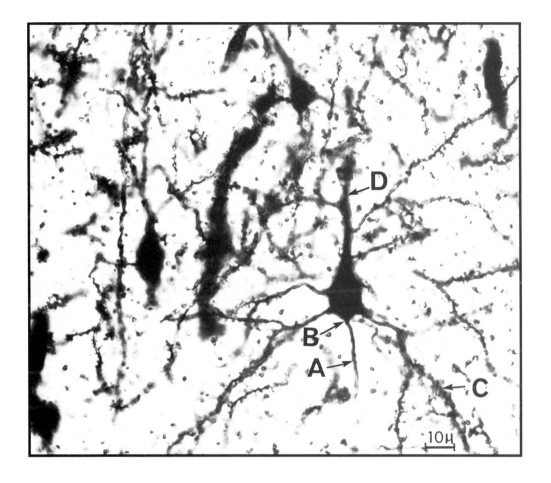

A: axon of pyramidal cell
B: axon hillock
C: basal dendrite
D: apical dendrite

Figure 10. Pyramidal cells and processes in cerebral cortex.

In the late nineteenth century an Italian histologist, Camillo Golgi, discovered a remarkable effect in brain tissue that had been treated with potassium dichromate followed by silver nitrate. Occasional neurons (about one percent of those present) become completely impregnated with brown or black deposits, thereby demonstrating clearly all the morphological details of the affected cells. A variant of the original Golgi technique makes use of mercuric salts rather than silver nitrate.

Note that the apical dendrite of the neuron shown here was cut off by the plane of the section. Both apical and basal dendrites are covered with dendritic spines. The Golgi technique may impregnate glial cells and capillaries as well as neurons.

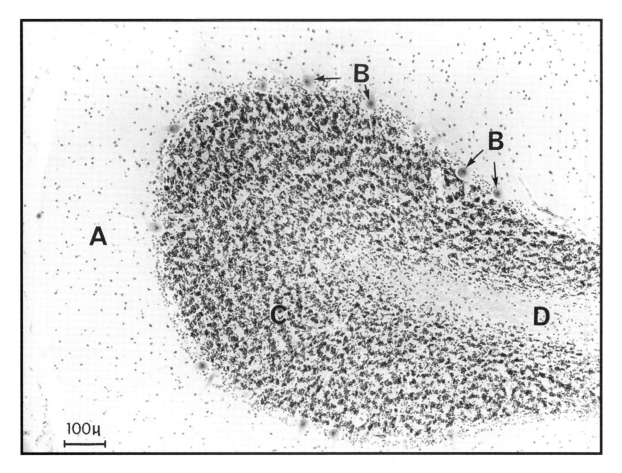

A: molecular layer
B: Purkinje cells
C: granule cell layer
D: white matter

Figure 11. Cross section through a folium of cerebellar cortex. Nissl stain.

The cerebellar cortex, like the cerebral cortex, has an outer molecular layer of fine cell processes and deeper cell layers. Small granule cells, present in vast numbers, provide inputs to the much less numerous Purkinje cells which are efferent neurons projecting outside the cerebellar cortex.

The cerebellar cortex is folded into numerous small folia (singular, folium, a leaf) and larger lobules. As in the cerebrum, the largest subdivisions of the cerebellum are called lobes.

The name "Purkinje cell" commemorates Johannes Purkinje, a nineteenth century Bohemian scientist.

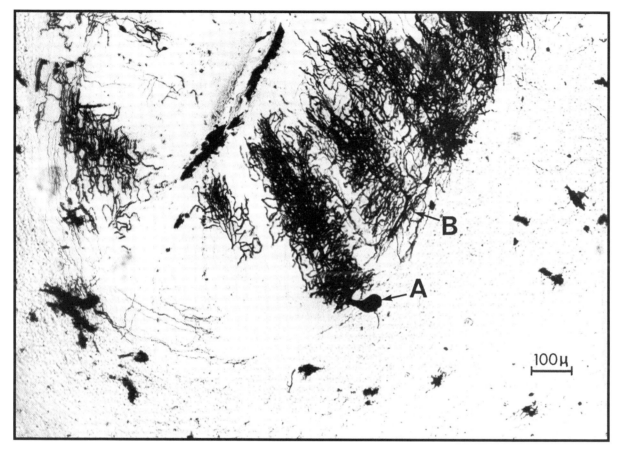

A: Purkinje cell soma
B: dendritic tree of
       another Purkinje
       cell

100µ

Figure 12. Purkinje cells in cerebellar cortex. Golgi preparation.

Purkinje cells have very characteristic large bushy dendrites. The dendrites are flattened and are arranged along a folium in somewhat the same way that dinner plates are stacked behind one another in a drying rack. Consequently, sections parallel to the long axis of a folium reveal them edge-on, while sections at right angles to this reveal their full extent.

In the example labelled "B", the cell body was cut off by the plane of the section.

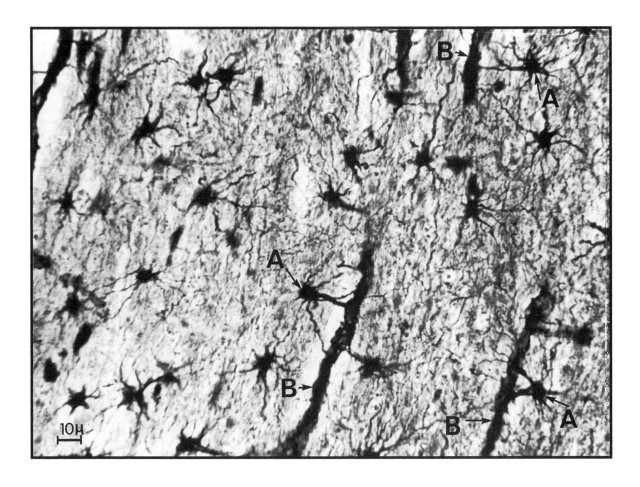

A: astrocytes
B: capillaries

Figure 13. Astrocytes

Astrocytes or "spider cells" are neuroglia that possess a number of processes radiating out from the cell body. Astrocytes form a network between blood vessels and neurons and are closely connected with both. Processes called "sucker feet" or "vascular feet" surround capillaries and also form networks around the somata and processes of neurones, leaving spaces for synapses. Astrocytes occur throught the central nervous system.

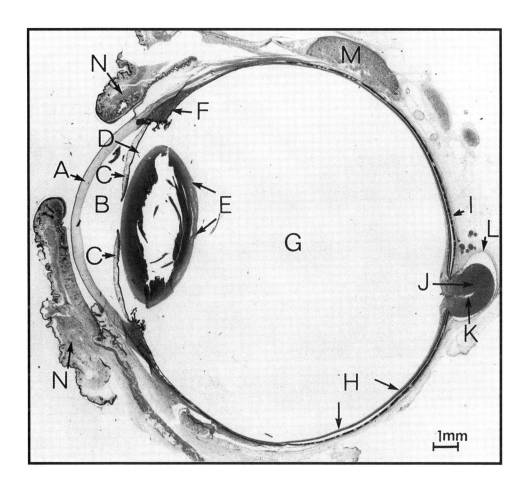

A:	cornea
B:	anterior chamber
C:	iris
D:	posterior chamber
E:	lens
F:	ciliary body or muscle
G:	vitreous humor or body
H:	retina
I:	sclera
J:	optic nerve
K:	central retinal vessels
L:	meninges surrounding optic nerve
M:	extrinsic ocular muscle
N:	eyelids

Figure 14. Cross section of a monkey eye.

The zonule, composed of fine fibers, connects the lens to the ciliary body. The lens was damaged during sectioning. The posterior chamber is bounded by the lens, the ciliary body, the vitreous humor, and the iris.

Contraction of the ciliary muscle reduces tension on the zonule, allowing the lens to assume its natural convex shape. When the zonule is under tension, as a result of relaxation of the ciliary muscle, the lens assumes a more flattened shape. Contraction of the ciliary body occurs during accomodation of the eye to a near object. The iris acts as a kind of sphincter, varying the amount of light entering the eye by varying the size of the pupil (a hole in the center of the iris).

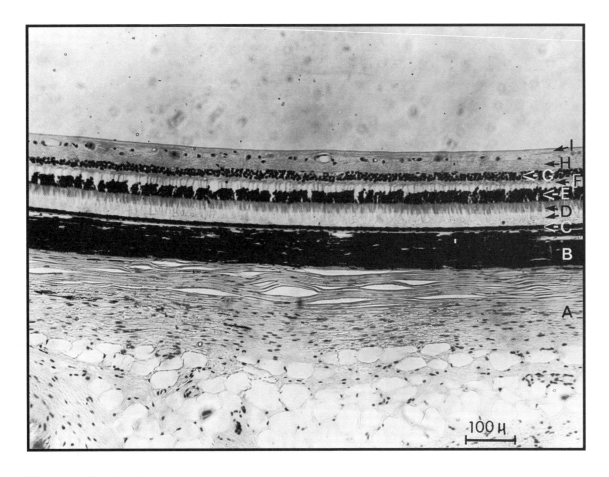

A:	sclera
B:	choroid
C:	pigmented epithelium
D:	receptor layer
E:	outer nuclear layer
F:	outer plexiform layer
G:	inner nuclear layer
H:	inner plexiform layer
I:	ganglion cell layer

Figure 15. Retina, choroid and sclera of monkey eye.

The sclera, the tough white outer coat of the eye, consists of connective tissue. In the anterior portion of the eye the sclera bulges foreward to form the cornea, which is transparent. The choroid contains many blood vessels and pigmented cells containing melanin. The receptor layer contains the photopigment - containing processes of the rods and cones whose cell bodies lie in the outer nuclear layer. In the outer plexiform layer, the axons of rods and cones synapse with bipolar cells and horizontal cells. The inner nuclear layer contains the cell bodies of the bipolar cells and the horizontal cells. In the inner plexiform layer, the bipolar cells synapse with ganglion cells whose somata lie in the ganglion cell layer. The axons of the ganglion cells run on the inner surface of the ganglion cell layer en route to their exit from the eye via the optic nerve.

It should be noted that light rays, focussed on the retina by the refractive power of the cornea and lens, must pass through several layers of neural tissue before reaching the light sensitive elements in the rods and cones.

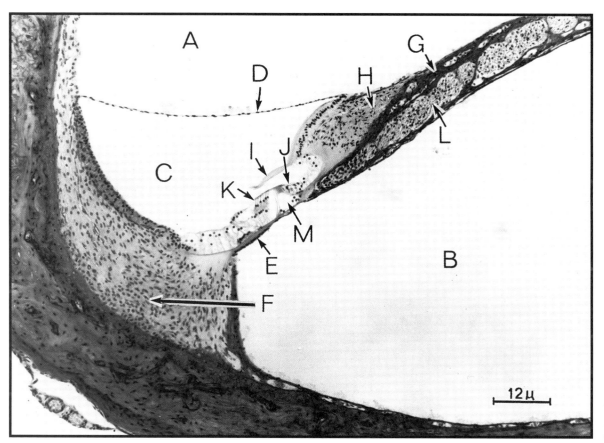

A: scala vestibuli
B: scala tympani
C: cochlear duct (or scala media)
D: Reissner's membrane
E: basilar membrane
F: spiral ligament
G: osseous spiral lamina
H: spiral limbus
I: tectorial membrane
J: inner hair cells
K: outer hair cells
L: cochlear nerve
M: tunnel of Corti

12 μ

Figure 16. Cross-section of the cochlea, parallel to the modiolus.

The cochlea is a bony tube wound in a spiral around a central bony pillar, the modiolus. A hollow spiral shelf, formed by the basilar membrane, the osseous spiral lamina and Reissner's membrane, divides the lumen of this tube into 2 parts, the scala vestibuli and the scala tympani. The scala vestibuli and scala tympani are normally filled with endolymph. Rapid movements of the tympanic membrane (ear drum), acting via the tympanic ossicles (malleus, incus, and stapes; not shown) exert pressure on one end of the scala vestibuli (at the oval window). As a result, the elastic parts of the cochlear partition, including the basilar membrane, bulge outwards or inwards. Since the tectorial membrane is stiffer than the basilar membrane, relative movement of the two takes place. Since the projecting hairs (cilia) of the hair cells are enmeshed in the tectorial membrane while the hair cells bodies are located on the basilar membrane, the cilia are bent to and fro. This results in receptor potentials and transmitter release which in turn, excites the processes of auditory nerve fibers. Owing to a technical artifact, the hair cells in Figure 16 have been separated from the tectorial membrane.

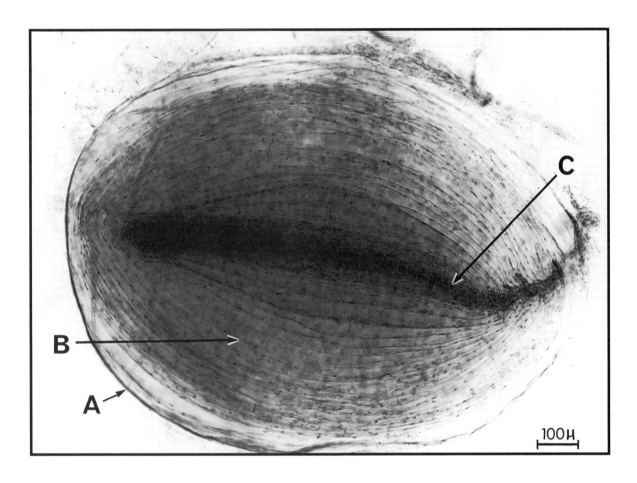

A: capsule
B: core
C: nerve fiber

100μ

Figure 17. Pacinian corpuscle.

This is a type of mechanoreceptor widely distributed in the skin, joint capsules, mesenteries and urinary bladder. It is an oval structure, 1-4 mm long, consisting of a capsule, a core , and a nerve fiber. The capsule consists of connective tissue. The core consists of large numbers of flattened cells (probably modified Schwann cells) arranged to form a series of concentric layers, somewhat like an onion. The nuclei of these cells can be seen. The nerve fiber supplying the corpuscle is myelinated, but the myelin coat does not extend into the capsule. Pressure on the capsule results in deformation and excitation of the nerve fiber.

A great variety of sense organs exist in the skin. Some, like the Pacinian corpuscle, end in capsules of some sort. Included in this group are Meissner's corpuscles, Ruffini's corpuscles, and Krause's end bulbs. In other cases, the afferent nerve fiber branches out into numerous fine terminals (free nerve endings). Nerve fibers may also spiral around the root of a hair, providing sensory input whenever the hair is moved.

Much research has been devoted to attempts to correlate particular types of skin receptors with specific modalities of sensory input such as pain, pressure, light touch, etc.

Appendix III: Brain circuits

Appendix III: Brain circuits

Introduction

The following diagrams and text are intended to provide a functional dimension to dissection and study of the sheep brain. Since the sheep has not been a popular subject of study in neuroscience, the material is based largely on investigations in other mammalian species, including man. Where possible, however, the results of studies on the sheep brain have been presented.

The cranial nerves.

The cranial nerves in mammals are conventionally numbered from I - XII beginning with the most rostral. Since many of these nerves are discussed in more detail in the diagrams that follow, only a brief list is provided here.

I. Olfactory nerve: consists of olfactory afferents. Note that the axons of the olfactory nerves are torn off when the olfactory bulb is removed from the skull and only the bulb remains attached to the rest of the brain.

II. Optic nerve: consists of visual afferents.

III. Oculomotor nerve.

IV. Trochlear nerve.

V. Trigeminal nerve. This nerve provides a general afferent input from the head and a motor output to muscles involved in mastication.

VI. Abducens nerve. The oculomotor, trochlear, and abducens nerves together provide the motor innervation of the extra-ocular muscles which rotate the eye in its socket. In addition, the oculomotor nerve supplies a parasympathetic input to the ciliary muscle (for accommodation) and to the sphincter muscle of the pupil (constricting it) plus an input to a muscle which raises the eyelid (levator palpebrae superioris).

VII. Facial nerve. Components of this nerve include: a motor innervation of the facial muscles, a parasympathetic input to the salivary and lacrimal glands, plus taste afferents.

VIII. Vestibulo-cochlear nerve: sensory fibers from the cochlea and vestibular apparatus.

IX. Glossopharyngeal nerve.

X. Vagus nerve. Nerves IX and X supply a motor input to the soft palate, pharynx and larynx which is important in respiration, vocalization and swallowing. Taste afferents run in both nerves, especially IX. Both nerves also carry sensory input from visceral structures such as the carotid sinus, carotid body, and lungs. The glossopharyngeal nerve provides a parasympathetic innervation to the parotid (salivary) gland while the vagus nerve provides a parasympathetic innervation to thoracic and abdominal viscera such as the bronchioles, heart and stomach.

XI. Spinal accessory nerve. This nerve contributes to movements of the shoulder and head as a result of a motor innervation of the trapezius and sternocleidomastoid muscles.

XII. Hypoglossal nerve. This is a pure motor nerve innervating tongue muscles (genioglossus and geniohyoid muscles, intrinsic muscles of the tongue).

Figure 1. Somatosensory afferents: The dorsal column pathway.

Left, schematic horizontal section through brain and spinal cord; Right, coronal sections through the cervical spinal cord, medulla and thalamus. **1**, the axon of a lumbar dorsal root ganglion cell (supplying the hind limb) enters the cord, bifurcates into a short descending branch and a longer ascending branch which passes to the medulla via the dorsal columns; **2**, a similar axon, conveying afferent input from the forelimb enters the cord at a cervical level. In addition to the long ascending branches, both afferent fibers make extensive contact with spinal neurons near the point of entry into the cord. Afferent axons entering in the sacral, lumbar, and lower thoracic levels of the cord run in the fasciculus gracilis (or gracile fasciculus, **8**) but those that enter the cord at upper thoracic or cervical levels run in the fasciculus cuneatus (or cuneate fasciculus, **9**). The ascending dorsal column fibers make synaptic contact with secondary neurons in the dorsal column nuclei which include the nucleus gracilis (or gracile nucleus, **3**), and the nucleus cuneatus (or cuneate nucleus, **4**). The secondary neurons decussate and take up a position in the ventromedial medulla forming a tract known as the medial lemniscus (**7**). Fibers in the medial lemniscus reach the thalamus and make synaptic contact with thalamocortical projection neurons (**5,6**) especially in the nucleus ventralis postero-lateralis (VPL or postero-lateral ventral nucleus). These cells, in turn, send axons through the internal capsule (**15**, lying between the caudate nucleus, **13**, and the putamen, **14**) and corona radiata (interdigitating with fibers of the corpus callosum) to make synaptic contact with cells in the neocortical somatosensory areas (**11,12**, see Figure 6). Thalamocortical fibers tend to end in bushy arbors in the internal granular layer (layer 4) of the neocortex. From the spinal cord to the neocortex, the dorsal column system displays a high degree of somatotopic or point-to-point projection, which means that the body surface is mapped out topographically. Thus, in the spinal cord the hind limb fibers are medial to trunk fibers which are, in turn medial to forelimb fibers. In the thalamus the order tends to be reversed: The medial-lateral sequence is forelimb, trunk, hind limb. Cells of the dorsal column system are activated by tactile stimuli of the appropriate body part. Interruption of the dorsal columns results in a loss of complex tactile discriminations (such as the ability to recognize letters traced on the skin in humans, or the ability to discriminate different roughnesses of sandpaper) and the ability to regulate the force of the hand grip (humans and monkeys). The ability to sense vibration is also lost.

An additional somatosensory system, functionally similar to the dorsal column system, includes ascending fibers in the dorsolateral fasciculus (**10**) which carry afferent information from the hind limb, a synaptic relay in the lateral cervical nucleus (in the cervical cord), and ascending projections to VPL. Section of both the dorsolateral fasciculus and the dorsal columns at a cervical level results in a loss of a sense of position (proprioception) in both upper and lower limbs. Section of the dorsal columns at a thoracic level will affect input only from the lower limbs.

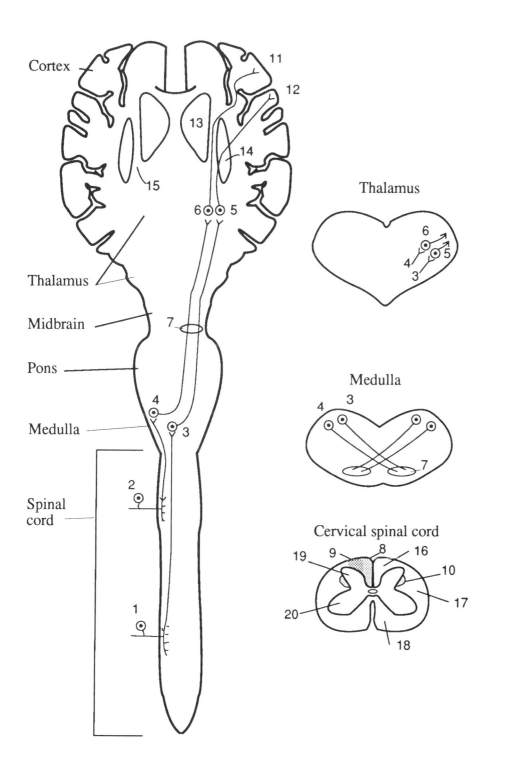

Cortex

11

12

13

14

15

6 ⊙⊙ 5

Thalamus

Thalamus

Midbrain

7

Pons

Medulla

4

3

Spinal cord

2

1

Thalamus

6
4 5
3

Medulla

4 3

7

Cervical spinal cord

19 9 8 16
10
20 17
18

Figure 1.

1&2:	dorsal root ganglion cells
3:	projection neuron, gracile nucleus
4:	projection neuron, cuneate nucleus
5&6:	projection neurons, nucleus ventralis posterolateralis of the thalamus
7:	medial lemniscus
8:	gracile fasciculus
9:	cuneate fasciculus
10:	dorsolateral fasciculus
11&12:	somatosensory projection areas in neocortex
13:	caudate nucleus
14:	putamen
15:	internal capsule
16:	dorsal column
17:	lateral column
18:	ventral column
19:	dorsal horn
20:	ventral horn

Figure 2. Somatosensory afferents: The spinothalamic pathway.

1, a small diameter dorsal root fiber enters the cord and bifurcates into short descending and ascending branches which run in Lissauer's tract for a few segments and make multiple synaptic contacts with spinal neurons. Some of these neurons **(2,3)** give rise to long axons which soon decussate in the ventral white commissure **(12)** and ascend in the ventral and lateral spinal columns and in the lateral part of the medulla **(10,** hatched region) lateral to the medial lemniscus **(9).** In the thalamus, synaptic contact is made with neurons in the ventral nucleus **(5,** VPL) and also with neurons in the intralaminar nuclei **(4,** nuclei interspersed with the fibers of the internal medullary lamina of the thalamus). The VPL neurons project to the neocortical somatosensory area **(8)** but the main projection of the intralaminar nuclei is to the caudate nucleus **(6)** and putamen **(7).**

Accompanying the spinothalamic pathway are direct or collateral projections to the medullary and pontine reticular formation (spinoreticular fibers) and to the tectum (spinotectal fibers). All these systems appear to convey information concerning temperature, noxious or potentially noxious stimuli (pain), itch and tickle as well as general tactile information. The powerful capacity of noxious stimuli to elicit generalized motor activity (as opposed to local spinal reflexes) may be due to activation of tectospinal and reticulospinal fibers (see figure 4). Projections to the intralaminar nuclei may influence motor activity via an input to the striatum (see Figure 8). Surgical section of the ascending spinothalamic, spinoreticular and spinotectal pathways (ventrolateral cordotomy) is sometimes used for the relief of severe chronic pain. Following such surgery, pain and temperature sense may be lost contralaterally caudal to the level of the section but tactile sensibility persists bilaterally because the dorsal columns are intact.

Making use of the information in Figures 1 and 2, what would be the sensory consequences of hemi-section of the spinal cord (Brown-Sequard syndrome) or of destruction of the ventral white commissure? The latter condition occurs in syringomyelia, a disorder in which tissue surrounding the spinal central canal is slowly destroyed.

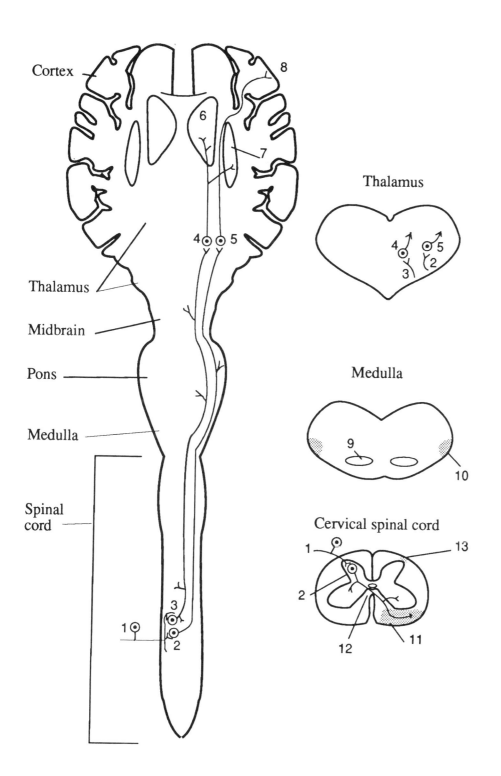

Cortex

8

6

7

Thalamus

Midbrain

Pons

Medulla

Spinal
cord

4 ⊙ ⊙ 5

1 ⊙

3
⊙
⊙
2

Thalamus

4 ⊙↗ ⊙↗ 5

3 2

Medulla

9

10

Cervical spinal cord

1 ⊙   13

2

12   11

Figure 2.

1:	dorsal root ganglion cell
2&3:	spinothalamic neurons
4:	thalamostriate projection neuron
5:	thalamocortical projection neuron
6:	caudate nucleus
7:	putamen
8:	neocortical somatosensory areas
9:	medial lemniscus
10:	location of spinothalamic pathway in medulla
11:	location of spinothalamic pathway in spinal cord
12:	ventral white commissure
13:	Lissauer's tract

Figure 3. Somatosensory afferents: The trigeminal pathways.

1,2,3, afferent neurons whose somata lie in the trigeminal or Gasserian ganglion outside the brain. The trigeminal nerve is grossly divisible into ophthalmic, maxillary and mandibular parts, plus a motor root. Its afferent fibers carry input from mechanoreceptors, proprioceptors, thermoceptors, and nociceptors in the face and jaw. The ophthalmic division of the trigeminal innervates the eye, part of the nose and the anterior scalp; the maxillary division innervates the upper jaw; the mandibular division innervates the lower jaw and part of the temple. Some of the trigeminal afferents synapse with neurons in the principal trigeminal nucleus in the pons. Secondary fibers from cells in this nucleus project both ipsilaterally (**5**) and contralaterally (**6**) to the thalamic nucleus ventralis posteromedialis (VPM). Thalamocortical projections then ascend without further decussation (**8,9,10**) to the corresponding somatosensory areas in the neocortex (**13,14**). In sheep and other ungulates the ipsilateral projections predominate but in most other mammals that have been studied (including man) the contralateral pathway predominates. An important component of trigeminal afferents course in a caudal direction from their point of entry, forming the spinal tract of the trigeminal nerve (**4**). Fibers in this tract descend as far as the upper cervical segments of the cord and make synaptic contact with secondary neurons in the associated spinal nucleus of the trigeminal nerve. The secondary neurons (**7**) send ascending fibers to the contralateral or ipsilateral (not shown) thalamic VPM and intralaminar nuclei. There are also projections to the brain stem reticular formation. The pathways passing via the principal trigeminal nucleus are comparable to the dorsal column pathway of the spinal cord, and appear to mediate mainly tactile information. Correspondingly, the spinal tract of the trigeminal corresponds to Lissauer's tract and its secondary projections correspond to the spinothalamic pathway. Like the spinothalamic pathway, the projections from the spinal trigeminal nucleus carry pain and temperature inputs (in part, to the intralaminar nuclei, **9**) as well as tactile information. As a result of the segregation of inputs in the principal nucleus and the spinal tract and nucleus, section of the spinal tract caudal to the zone of entry of the trigeminal nerve (medullary tractotomy) can abolish painful input from the face without eliminating tactile input. Medullary tractotomy has been used successfully in the treatment of trigeminal neuralgia, a condition in which intermittent episodes of extreme pain occur in the face.

An additional sensory trigeminal pathway consists of proprioceptive fibers arising in jaw muscles, such as the masseter and temporalis (not shown). The cell bodies of these afferent fibers are unusual in that they are located in the midbrain (mesencephalic nucleus of the trigeminal nerve) and make monosynaptic contacts with motoneurons in the motor nucleus of the trigeminal nerve (**15**). The motor root of the trigeminal, carrying fibers from the motor nucleus, innervates the jaw muscles.

Finally, it should be mentioned that some somatosensory fibers that enter the brain via the facial, glossopharyngeal, and vagus nerves join the spinal tract of the trigeminal nerve and synapse with secondary ascending trigeminal projection neurons.

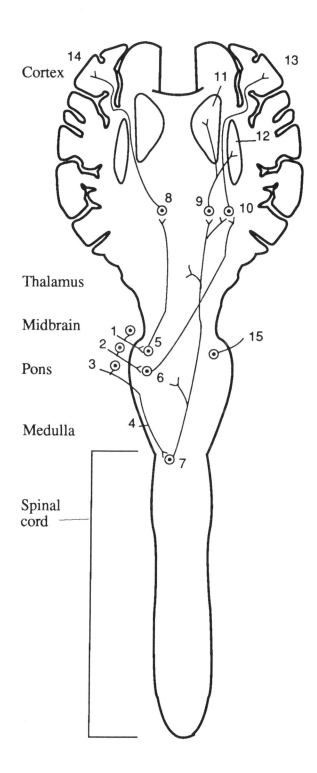

Figure 3.

1,2&3:	trigeminal afferent neurons
4:	spinal tract of trigeminal nerve
5,6&7:	secondary ascending trigeminal neurons
8,9&10:	thalamocortical projection neurons
11:	caudate nucleus
12:	putamen
13&14:	face areas of somatosensory cortex
15:	efferent neuron from motor nucleus of the trigeminal nerve

Figure 4. Descending pathways for gross movements of the head, trunk, hip and shoulder.

Left, dorsal view of brainstem; Right, cross sections of medulla and spinal cord. A, a spinal afferent fiber enters the cord and bifurcates into a short descending branch and a longer ascending branch. A monosynaptic contact with a ventral horn cell or motoneuron (2) is made in the left side of the diagram, creating a monosynaptic reflex arc, but in the spinal cross section the afferent effect on the motoneuron is shown mediated via an interneuron or local circuit neuron (3), creating a disynaptic reflex arc. Motoneuron # 1, located in the ventromedial part of the ventral horn, projects to proximal muscles, i.e., those acting on the neck and trunk or the shoulder and hip joints. Motoneuron # 2, located in the dorsolateral part of the ventral horn, projects to the more distal muscles especially those controlling the limb extremities. Descending fibers from the brain stem to the spinal cord include vestibulospinal fibers (4), reticulospinal fibers (5,6) and tectospinal fibers (7) which control, primarily, motoneurons in the ventromedial part of the ventral horn. Tectospinal fibers originate in the superior colliculus. Descending axons are shown from one side only, to avoid complicating the diagram. Tectospinal projections are mainly crossed or contralateral while vestibulospinal projections are mainly uncrossed or ipsilateral. Reticulospinal fibers from the medullary reticular formation project bilaterally while those from the pontine reticular formation project mainly ipsilaterally. The descending fibers are shown ending on interneurons, an arrangement that permits control of movement via the reflex circuitry of the spinal cord. However, some descending brain stem fibers act directly on motoneurons as well. Reticulospinal fibers arise from the ventromedial part of the brain stem (hatched lines in the cross section of the medulla, 9). The vestibular nuclei are also shown (8).

In the cross section of the spinal cord the reticulospinal fibers and vestibulospinal fibers are shown descending in the ventral column. Some reticulospinal fibers descend in the lateral columns. The termination of both sets of fibers is in the ventromedial part of the ventral horn (14). This pattern of projections contrasts with that of the corticospinal and rubrospinal projections which run mainly in the lateral columns (13) terminate in the dorsolateral part of the ventral horn and the base of the dorsal horn (15). Reticulospinal and tectospinal cells receive inputs from many sources, including descending fibers from the cerebral cortex. These descending pathways are probably mostly not monosynaptic. Vestibulospinal neurons appear not to receive direct inputs from the cerebral cortex.

The capacity of the descending brain stem projections to control motor activity is demonstrated by the fact that removal of the neocortical motor areas, or of the entire cerebral cortex, has only minimal effects on gross movement patterns such as walking, running, or swimming, in most mammals. Tectospinal fibers, which project mainly to the cervical cord, appear to be involved mainly in head and eye movements; vestibulospinal and reticulospinal pathways appear to control posture and locomotion. Large lesions of the medial brain stem abolish locomotion and righting responses, probably as a result of destruction of these descending projections to the ventromedial part of the ventral horn of the spinal cord.

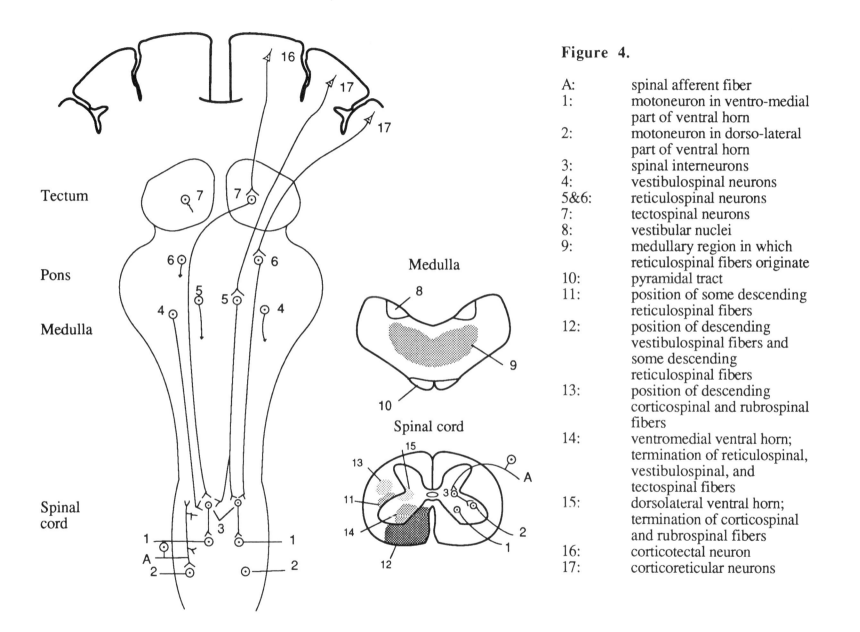

Figure 4.

A:	spinal afferent fiber
1:	motoneuron in ventro-medial part of ventral horn
2:	motoneuron in dorso-lateral part of ventral horn
3:	spinal interneurons
4:	vestibulospinal neurons
5&6:	reticulospinal neurons
7:	tectospinal neurons
8:	vestibular nuclei
9:	medullary region in which reticulospinal fibers originate
10:	pyramidal tract
11:	position of some descending reticulospinal fibers
12:	position of descending vestibulospinal fibers and some descending reticulospinal fibers
13:	position of descending corticospinal and rubrospinal fibers
14:	ventromedial ventral horn; termination of reticulospinal, vestibulospinal, and tectospinal fibers
15:	dorsolateral ventral horn; termination of corticospinal and rubrospinal fibers
16:	corticotectal neuron
17:	corticoreticular neurons

Figure 5. Descending pathways for fine movements of the extremities.

Corticospinal fibers pass in succession through the internal capsule, the base of the cerebral peduncle (basis pedunculi, crura cerebri), the pons, and the pyramidal tract. In the lower medulla, most of the corticospinal fibers decussate and descend in the lateral spinal column (see Figure 4) but some descend ipsilaterally in the ventral column. In primates, some corticospinal fibers synapse monosynaptically with ventral horn cells in the dorsolateral ventral horn; others end on spinal interneurons. In animals such as sheep, which lack finely differentiated control of the extremities, monosynaptic corticospinal connections may not exist. Axons from neurons in the red nucleus (nucleus ruber) decussate and descend in the lateral spinal columns. Corticorubral projections permit cortical control of activity in the red nucleus. Corticobulbar fibers decussate and project to cranial nerve motor nuclei such as the facial nucleus. These descending connections may be made directly to motor neurons (as shown) or may be made to interneurons.

Destruction of corticospinal and rubrospinal pathways produces impairment in behaviors in which parts of the extremities are moved in isolation. Thus, the capacity to pick up and manipulate objects is impaired but gross movements such as walking are relatively unaffected. It may be that descending monosynaptic projections of corticospinal neurons on ventral horn cells are of especial importance in fine isolated movements of the digits in primates. In ungulates, such as the sheep, isolated movements of the digits are not possible. Consequently, the corticospinal tract is poorly developed in ungulates in comparison with primates or rodents which use the forepaws (or the hands) in manipulation. Projections from the neocortex to cranial motor nuclei, such as the oculomotor (and the trochlear and abducens nuclei), facial or hypoglossal nuclei, are believed to provide the basis for higher level control of eye, face and tongue movements, respectively.

Following extensive cortical lesions, human patients may lose voluntary control of movements even though more automatic movements of the same body part remain intact. Thus, a patient who cannot protrude the tongue outside the lips when asked to do so may be able to lick water from the lips without any difficulty. Patients who cannot show their teeth upon request may show normal, or even exaggerated, movements of the lips when laughing. Failure to comply with verbal requests in such cases is not always due to failure to understand what is wanted since the patients may use their fingers to move the body part that they cannot control directly.

These phenomena illustrate an important principle of neural organization. The patterns of muscular contraction that produce many common behaviors are controlled by circuits in the brainstem, cerebellum and spinal cord. Normally, such subcortical "motor programs" are controlled by the cerebral cortex, thus permitting an adaptive high level control of behavior. However, after cerebral damage, higher level control is impaired and the lower level programs operate independently. For example, a decorticate rat can walk perfectly well but its walking is aimless, poorly related to physiological needs and external circumstances. Extensive destruction of the cerebral cortex in humans does not interfere with spontaneous breathing but the special control of the respiratory apparatus that is essential to speech is abolished.

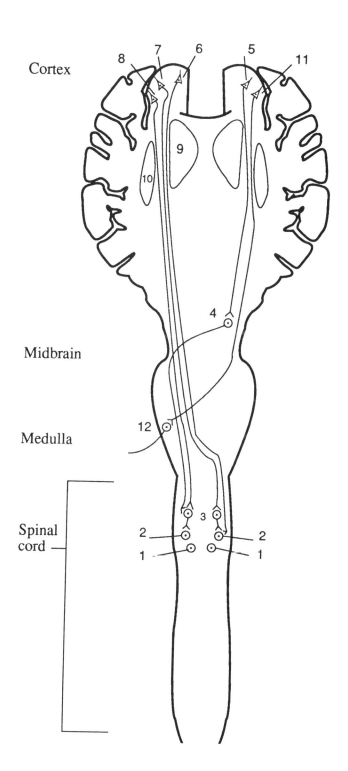

Cortex

Midbrain

Medulla

Spinal
cord

Figure 5.

1:	motoneuron in ventro-medial part of ventral horn
2:	motoneuron in dorso-lateral part of ventral horn
3:	spinal interneurons
4:	rubrospinal neuron
5:	corticorubral neuron
6:	decussating corticospinal neuron with monosynaptic connection to ventral horn cell
7:	decussating corticospinal neuron with connection to spinal interneuron
8:	non-decussating corticospinal neuron with connection to spinal interneuron
9:	caudate nucleus
10:	putamen
11:	decussating corticobulbar neuron projecting to the facial nucleus
12:	facial nucleus motoneuron

Figure 6.   Localization of function in the neocortex of the sheep.

These maps of sensory and motor areas are based on studies in anesthetized sheep. The motor area is defined as the region where relatively weak electrical stimulation will elicit visible movement; the visual and auditory areas are those in which slow wave evoked potentials or multiunit activity can be elicited by flashes of light or clicks, respectively. The somatosensory areas give rise to evoked responses following light touches of the skin surface. In most mammals the parts of the body are represented at least twice (somatosensory areas 1 and 2, S1 and S2; motor areas 1 and 2). The primary cortical motor area extends on to the medial surface of the hemisphere for a short distance. A second motor area, present on the medial surface of the hemisphere in many mammals (the supplementary motor area), has not yet been described in the sheep.

Cortical areas that lie outside the motor cortex and the direct sensory receiving areas are traditionally referred to as "association areas", apparently on the assumption that the "association of ideas" takes place there. However, recent studies in other mammals show that essentially the entire neocortex receives inputs from sensory receptors and that there are no association areas in the traditional sense. Further, "motor" areas receive sensory inputs and, especially in unanesthetized animals, movements can be elicited by stimulation of sensory areas.

Although sensory surfaces are represented topographically in the neocortex, some areas have larger inputs than others. Thus, the fovea has a larger cortical representation than the rest of the retina. In the case of the somatosensory representation of a grazing animal such as the sheep, the lips, tongue, teeth, and face have a much larger representation, in both the thalamus and the neocortex, than the limbs.   In humans, the lips, tongue and fingers have very large representations in both the pre-and post-central gyri (see Figure 17). It is apparent that body parts with highly differentiated sensory and motor capabilities have larger neural representations than body parts with less differentiated functions. The particular representations that are highly developed vary from species to species, in accordance with their respective modes of existence.

All the regions of the neocortex appear to receive input from some part of the thalamus. However, the neocortex also receives inputs from non-thalamic structures. Among these are cholinergic afferents that originate in the basal forebrain (substantia innominata, nucleus basalis of Meynert) and serotonergic afferents that originate in the midbrain and upper pons. These inputs appear to exert a generalized regulatory control over neocortical activity while the thalamic afferents convey specific information about sensory events. The neocortex also receives a diffuse noradrenergic input from the locus coeruleus (in the dorsal pons) but its functional significance remains obscure. There is some evidence suggesting noradrenergic involvement in cortical neuroplasticity.

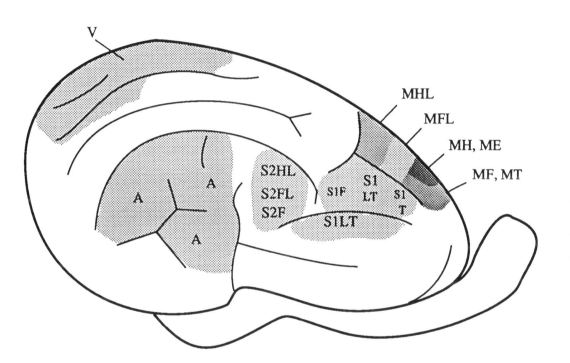

Figure 6.

A: auditory areas
ME: motor area for eyes
MF: motor area for face
MFL: motor area for forelimb
MH: motor area for head
MHL: motor area for hind limb
MT: motor area for tongue
S1F: face area in somatosensory
            area I
S1LT: lip and tongue area in
            somatosensory area I
S1T: tongue area in
            somatosensory area I
S2F: face area in somatosensory
            area II
S2FL: forelimb area in
            somatosensory area II
S2HL: hind limb area in
            somatosensory area II
V: visual cortex

Figure 7. Neuronal circuits involving the cerebellum.

A dorsal root ganglion cell (1) makes synaptic contact with a spinocerebellar neuron (2) whose axon ascends through the restiforme body (inferior cerebellar peduncle) and makes synaptic contact with granule cells (5) in the cerebellar cortex. The granule cells, in turn, synapse with Purkinje cells (6) whose axons project to the deep cerebellar nuclei. The latter include the dentate nucleus (7) and the fastigial nucleus (8). Fastigial neurons project largely to the reticular formation and vestibular nuclei where they are in a position to influence reticulospinal and vestibulospinal projections (9). A second pathway includes a dorsal root ganglion cell (1a) input to a spino-olivary neuron (3) that projects to the inferior olive. An olivary neuron (4) sends an ascending axon to the cerebellar cortex (via the restiform body) where synaptic contact is made with the extensive dendritic tree of the Purkinje cell (6). Olivo-cerebellar fibers end on the Purkinje dendrites in a pattern resembling a vine climbing on a trellis (climbing fibers). Other afferents to the cerebellar cortex end in clusters of fine fibers (rosettes) referred to as mossy fibers. The synapses referred to so far are excitatory with the exception of the Purkinje cell effect on cells in the deep cerebellar nuclei (7,8) which is usually inhibitory. However, the circuits shown here are greatly simplified, ignoring for example, the presence of additional neurons (basket cells, Golgi cells) located in the cerebellar cortex.

Cerebellar circuits involving the forebrain can be thought of as beginning with a corticopontine projection which originates from pyramidal cells in layer V in widespread regions of the neocortex (14,15). The axons, descending ipsilaterally through the internal capsule and cerebral peduncle, make synaptic contact with neurons in the pons (16) whose axons project to the cerebellar cortex. There they synapse with granule cells (5) which excite Purkinje cells (6). The pontocerebellar system, projecting through the brachium pontis (middle cerebellar peduncle), is truly massive and probably plays a major role in the control of movement. The Purkinje cells can exert a strong effect on forebrain activity via projections to the dentate nuclei. Dentate cells send axons foreward through the brachium conjunctivum (superior cerebellar peduncle) to make contact with rubrospinal neurons (10) in the red nucleus and neurons in the thalamus. The thalamic recipients of dentate fibers consist of two main groups. First, cells (11) in the ventral nucleus (especially nucleus ventralis lateralis) send fibers to the motor cortex where they may affect the firing of corticospinal, corticorubral, corticobulbar, corticopontine, corticoreticular, or corticotectal fibers (13, with heavy arrow indicating a descending output). Secondly, dentatothalamic fibers end on cells in the intralaminar nuclei (12) which project to the caudate nucleus and putamen. Via this pathway the cerebellum can influence the striatal circuitry outlined in Figure 8.

Removal of the entire cerebellum produces a generalized ataxia (loss of co-ordinated movement) but no real paralysis. Muscle tone is reduced, there is an impairment of balance (decerebellate animals walk with a wide base), tremor occurs during movement, and there is a tendency for movements to overshoot the mark.

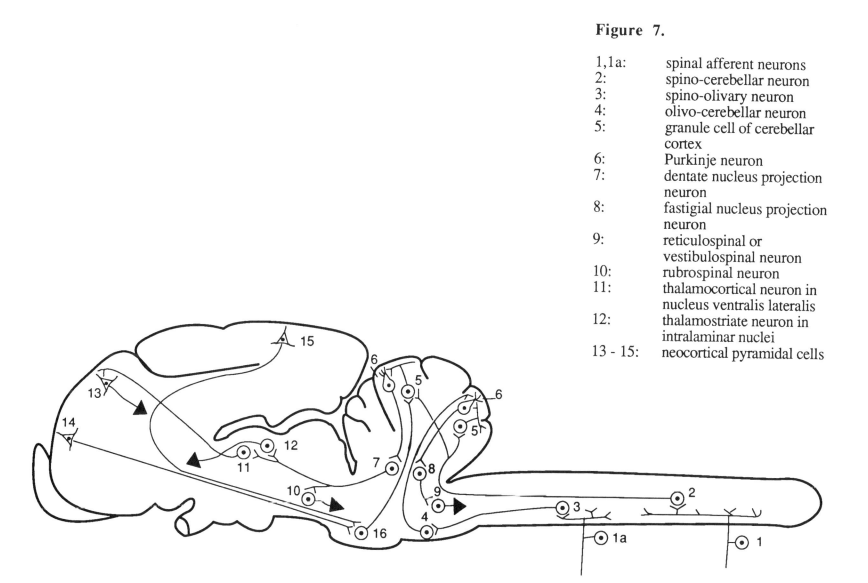

Figure 7.

1,1a: spinal afferent neurons
2:      spino-cerebellar neuron
3:      spino-olivary neuron
4:      olivo-cerebellar neuron
5:      granule cell of cerebellar cortex
6:      Purkinje neuron
7:      dentate nucleus projection neuron
8:      fastigial nucleus projection neuron
9:      reticulospinal or vestibulospinal neuron
10:      rubrospinal neuron
11:      thalamocortical neuron in nucleus ventralis lateralis
12:      thalamostriate neuron in intralaminar nuclei
13 - 15:   neocortical pyramidal cells

Figure 8. Neuronal circuits involving the basal ganglia.

Neurons in pars compacta of the substantia nigra send axons to the striatum (**9**,nigrostriatal fibers). Corticostriate fibers (**10**) from virtually all areas of the neocortex also project to the striatum, as do thalamostriate fibers (**11**) which originate primarily in the intralaminar nuclei. Efferents from the striatum (**12**) project to the globus pallidus and both divisions of the substantia nigra (striatopallidal and striatonigral fibers). The globus pallidus sends fibers to the substantia nigra (**13**) and to the nucleus ventralis lateralis (VL) of the thalamus (**14**). VL also receives inputs from the cerebellum (see Figure 7) and the substantia nigra (**16**) and projects to the motor cortex (**15**). Further, the substantia nigra projects to the superior colliculus (**17**).

One can envisage several circuits by which the basal ganglia can influence movement. Cortical, thalamic, and nigral inputs can all influence the activity of the striatum. Serotonergic inputs from the brain stem (not shown) also have an effect. From the striatum there are two main efferent pathways: (**A**) to the thalamus-motor cortex output via the globus pallidus or the pars reticulata of the substanta nigra; or (**B**) to the pars reticulata-tectospinal output via the globus pallidus or direct striatonigral projections to pars reticulata. Other pathways also exist. For example, Figure 8 does not include the subthalamic nucleus which has important connections with the globus pallidus and substantia nigra.

Neurological syndromes associated with destruction of neurons in the basal ganglia in man include athetosis, chorea, hemiballismus, and Parkinson's disease. Destruction of the substantia nigra or striatum unilaterally in laboratory animals results in a tendency to walk in circles toward the side of the lesion (ipsiversive circling).

Understanding of these behavioral deficits has advanced rapidly in recent years as a result of discoveries in neuropharmacology and neurochemistry. The nigrostriatal pathway includes many dopaminergic neurons (those that synthesize and release dopamine). Interneurons in the striatum (not shown here) are cholinergic while the striatonigral and striatopallidal projections synthesize and release γ-aminobutyric acid. One of the results of this knowledge is the availability of new pharmacological treatments for several types of movement disorders in humans.

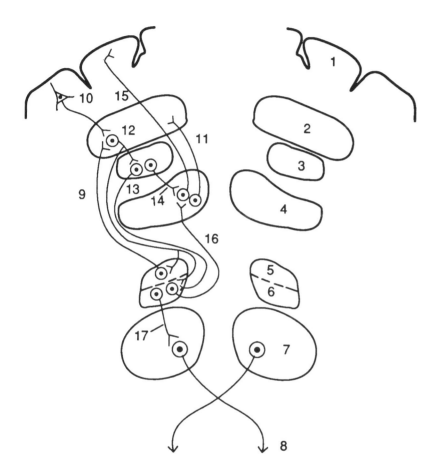

Figure 8.

1: neocortex
2: striatum
3: globus pallidus
4: thalamus
5: substantia nigra, pars compacta
6: substantia nigra, pars reticulata
7: superior colliculus
8: tectospinal fibers
9: nigrostriatal neuron
10: corticostriatal neuron
11: thalamostriatal neuron
12: striatal efferent neuron
13&14: pallidal efferent neurons
15: thalamocortical projection neuron
16: nigrothalamic projection neuron
17: nigrotectal projection neuron

Figure 9.   Auditory pathways.

Axons of cochlear ganglion cells enter the medulla and synapse in the cochlear nuclei. Secondary auditory fibers may decussate via the trapezoid body (5) or the dorsal acoustic stria (not shown), which run just below the IVth ventricle, and may project rostrally as far as the inferior colliculus. However, many fibers from the cochlear nuclei project ipsilaterally (3) or contralaterally (4) to the superior olive. The ascending bundle of fibers from the cochlear and superior olivary nuclei runs in the lateral brain stem and is known as the lateral lemniscus. Further synaptic relays (in the nuclei of the lateral lemniscus), as well as decussations, occur along the course of the lateral leminscus (not shown in Figure 9). Lateral lemniscus fibers synapse with neurons in the inferior colliculus. Inferior collicular neurons project ipsilaterally or contralaterally (through the commissure of the inferior colliculus) to the medial geniculate body, running via the brachium of the inferior colliculus (8,10). Neurons of the medial geniculate body (or nucleus) project ipsilaterally to the auditory cortex. Although the auditory pathway is very complex, containing many more synaptic relays and decussations than are shown in Figure 9, the overall effect is that most projections are contralateral. Thus, the left ear is better represented in the right inferior colliculus and auditory cortex than is the right ear (and vice versa). Projections from the inferior colliculus to the superior colliculus (11) may be important in such behaviors as turning the head toward a sound source since tectospinal fibers could be activated in this way. The inferior colliculus also contributes fibers to the tectopontine tracts (9), as does the superior colliculus, providing a means by which auditory inputs can influence the cerebellum (via pontocerebellar pathways). The auditory cortex, which has corticopontine projections, may also affect cerebellar activity. Presumably, these pathways play a role in auditory control of motor activity.

An interesting feature of the auditory system is that there exists a series of descending projections which parallel the ascending ones. The final level of these projections is the olivocochlear bundle which sends fibers to the hair cells. The function of this system remains speculative.

Experimental studies in cats show that section of the lateral lemniscus produces virtually complete deafness but ablation of higher level structures has more selective effects. After large lesions of the auditory cortex, for example, discrimination of sounds of different frequencies is preserved but the ability to discriminate tonal patterns or the ability to walk toward the source of a sound is severely impaired or lost.

The vestibular component of the VIII th nerve (not shown) carries sensory information from the semi-circular canals, utricle, and saccule to the vestibular nuclei in the medulla and to the flocculonodular lobe (flocculus and nodulus) of the cerebellum. Secondary fibers originating in the vestibular nuclei project to the spinal cord, the cerebellum, the reticular formation and other structures. The vestibular inputs play an important role in the sense of balance and in the control of eye movements.

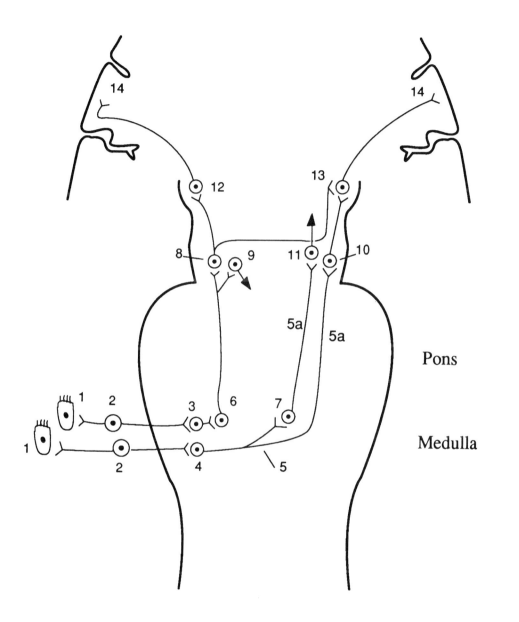

Figure 9.

1:	hair cells
2:	bipolar cells of the cochlear (or spiral) ganglion in the cochlea
3&4:	cells of the cochlear nuclei
5:	fibers of the trapezoid body
5a:	lateral lemniscus
6&7:	cells of the superior olive
8 - 11:	cells of the inferior colliculus
12&13:	cells of the medial geniculate body of the thalamus
14:	auditory areas of the neocortex

Figure 10. Visual Pathways.

Top, horizontal view of the geniculostriate pathway. Axons of retinal ganglion cells penetrate the wall of the eye ball at the optic disk and run to the lateral geniculate nucleus. Ganglion cells in the nasal hemi-retina (**1**) project to the contralateral lateral geniculate after decussation in the optic chiasm; those in the temporal hemi-retina (**2**) project to the ipsilateral lateral geniculate. Geniculo-striate fibers then project to the striate cortex (so named because of the presence of a band of myelinated fibers, the line of Gennari, that is present in the internal granular cell layer). Throughout these projections, there is an accurate retino-topic or point-to-point projection. The representation of the retina in the human brain is shown in Figure 17.

As a result of the partial decussation of the fibers from retinal ganglion cells, an object whose image falls on the left nasal hemi-retina and right temporal hemi-retina, will excite neurons in the right geniculo-striate system. Destruction of the right optic tract, or the right geniculo-striate pathway, will block output from the left nasal hemi-retina and right temporal hemi-retina. Owing to the inversion of the retinal images (**a** illuminates a'; **b** illuminates b'; dashed lines represent the path of light rays), such lesions will result in a loss of vision in the left visual field in each eye (left homonymous hemianopsia). Similarly, objects in the right visual field will excite the left geniculostriate pathway and a lesion of the left optic tract or left geniculo-striate pathway will produce a loss of vision (scotoma) in the right visual field in each eye (right homonymous hemianopsia). If the fibers of the optic chiasma are sectioned in the mid-sagittal plane, output from the nasal retinae is cut off and a heteronymous hemianopsia results (loss of vision in the left visual field in the left eye and in the right visual field in the right eye; also known as tunnel vision). **Bottom.** Additional visual pathways. Some retinal ganglion cells (**7**) project to the suprachiasmatic nucleus of the hypothalamus, a pathway that appears to exert a strong effect on circadian rhythms. Visual inputs to the pretectal nuclei (**8**) just rostral to the superior colliculus excite a pretectal-oculomotor pathway (**9**) to the Edinger-Westphal nucleus in the midbrain. From there, preganglionic parasympathetic fibers run to the ciliary ganglion which is located in the orbit. Post-ganglionic neurons then cause constriction of the pupil (light reflex). Retinal ganglion cell inputs to the superior colliculus (**11**) may activate a tectothalamic pathway (**12**) which projects to the pulvinar. Ascending projections from the pulvinar (**13**) project to the peristriate cortex, a belt of tissue lying rostral and lateral to the striate cortex.

Visual inputs can affect motor activity via a number of pathways. Among these are: tectospinal fibers (**14**, influenced by retinocollicular inputs); descending fibers from visual cortex to the striatum, tectum, pons, and reticular formation; and cortico-cortical projections to temporal and frontal neocortex.

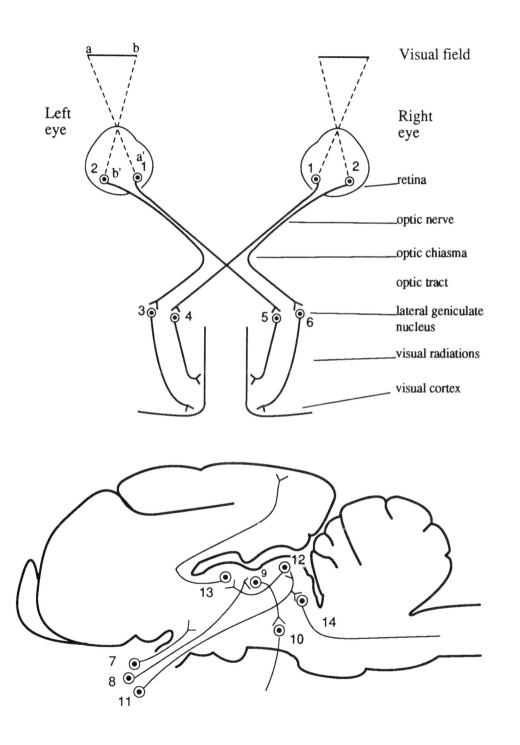

Visual field

Left eye

Right eye

retina

optic nerve

optic chiasma

optic tract

lateral geniculate nucleus

visual radiations

visual cortex

Figure 10.

a':   retinal projection of point a in external space

b':   retinal projection of point b in external space

1:      ganglion cell in nasal hemi-retina

2:      ganglion cell in temporal hemi-retina

3 - 6:   thalamocortical projection neurons

7:      retinal ganglion cell projecting to supra-chiasmatic nucleus

8:      retinal ganglion cell projecting to pretectal nuclei

9:      pretecto-oculomotor projection neuron

10:      preganglionic parasympathetic neuron in Edinger-Westphal nucleus

11:      retinal ganglion cell projecting to the superior colliculus

12:      tectopulvinar projection neuron

13:      thalamocortical projection neuron

14:      tectospinal neuron

Figure 11. Taste pathways.

The cell bodies of the afferent fibers lie in peripheral ganglia and make contact with taste buds in the anterior 2/3 of the tongue (facial nerve fibers) and posterior 1/3 of the tongue (glossopharyngeal fibers). In addition, some taste fibers from the palate and pharynx may enter the brain via the vagus nerve. The incoming afferents run in the solitary tract and synapse in the solitary nucleus. Secondary fibers ascend to the pontine taste area (parabrachial nucleus) which projects bilaterally to the most medial part of the posterior ventral nucleus. This, in turn, projects ipsilaterally to the cortical taste area which overlaps with or lies rostral to (in different species), the somatosensory face area. Lesions of any of these structures produce ageusia, an impairment of taste. Thus, animals with VPM lesions will drink quinine-flavored water that is normally rejected. Some fibers from the pontine taste area project to the hypothalamus, a pathway that might be involved in feeding.

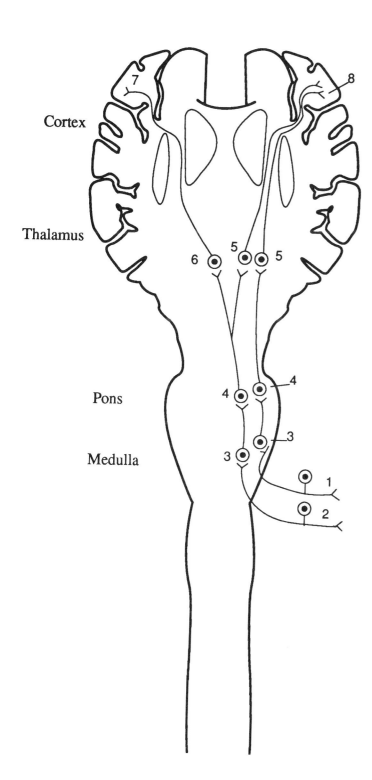

Cortex

Thalamus

Pons

Medulla

Figure 11.

1:        afferent fiber in facial nerve
2:        afferent fiber in
         glossopharyngeal nerve
3:        secondary taste fibers in
         solitary nucleus
4:        tertiary taste neurons in
         parabrachial nculeus
5&6:   thalamocortical neurons in
         nucleus ventralis
         posteromedialis (VPM)
7&8:   neocortical taste areas

Figure 12.   Olfactory pathways.

Ciliated olfactory receptors (**1**) provide olfactory nerve fibers that enter the olfactory bulb and make contact with mitral cells (**2**) and tufted cells (**3**). Axons from these cells pass via the lateral and medial olfactory tracts to the olfactory tubercle, almost the entire pyriform lobe (prepyriform cortex, periamygdaloid cortex, entorhinal cortex) as well as to the amygdala and hypothalamus. It is noteworthy that the olfactory input, unlike other sensory inputs, passes directly to a type of cortex (the pyriform lobe) and does not immediately involve the thalamus. However, since the amygdala and the periamygdaloid cortex project to the thalamus (to the nucleus medialis dorsalis, which in turn projects to parts of the frontal lobe), the thalamus might conceivably play some role in olfactory control of behavior. Since the entorhinal cortex projects to the dentate gyrus and hippocampus, the hippocampal formation may also be influenced by olfactory inputs.

An interesting feature of the olfactory bulb is that its projections are entirely ipsilateral, except for contralateral projections that cross the midline in the anterior commissure (not shown). If the anterior commissure is sectioned in humans and olfactory stimulation (e.g., an orange) is applied to the right nostril, the patient cannot name the source of the odor because the left hemisphere, which is the one usually involved in speech (see Figure 17), cannot receive olfactory input. However, the object corresponding to the odor (the orange) can be picked out from amongst other objects by the left hand. The right hemisphere, though usually mute, is evidently quite capable of recognising an orange.

Interhemispheric communication on visual, auditory, and somesthetic matters is mediated by the corpus callosum, a very large commissure interconnecting the right and left neocortices.

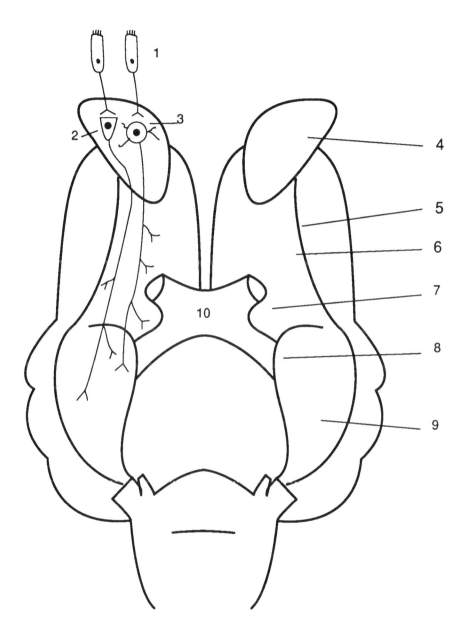

Figure 12.

1:      olfactory receptors
2:      mitral cell
3:      tufted cell
4:      olfactory bulb
5:      rhinal fissure
6:      prepyriform cortex
7:      olfactory tubercle
8:      periamygdaloid cortex
9:      entorhinal cortex
10:     optic chiasma

Figure 13.   Hippocampal formation.

The hippocampus, or Ammon's horn, the dentate gyrus, and subiculum comprise the hippocampal formation. The entorhinal cortex closely associated with the hippocampal formation, consists of the caudal part of the pyriform cortex. All are parts of the cerebral cortex.

The large pyramidal cells (3) of the hippocampus each possess extensive apical and basal dendrites and an axon which bifurcates, sending projections running both rostrally and caudally in the alveus, a white fiber layer that covers the surface of the hippocampus. Many pyramidal cells, therefore, project to both the septal nuclei and the subiculum, as well as other structures. The principal output of the hippocampal formation is the subiculum, a strip of cortex lying between the entorhinal cortex and Ammon's horn. Subicular cells send axons through the alveus and the pre-commissural fornix (rostral to the anterior commissure) and the post-commissural fornix (caudal to the anterior commissure) to reach the septal nuclei and the hypothalamus, especially the mammillary body. Septo-hypothalamic fibers, running in the medial forebrain bundle, provide an additional means by which hippocampal output can influence the hypothalamus. Descending projections from the mammillary body to the pons may provide an important pathway linking hippocampal output to the cerebellum, permitting hippocampal control of behavior.

The major afferent input to the hippocampal formation arises in the entorhinal cortex which sends fibers to the dentate gyrus and to Ammon's horn (not shown) via the perforant path, which runs through the subiculum. The entorhinal cortex, in turn, receives input from virtually the entire neocortex via a complex multisynaptic pathway. Thus, the hippocampal formation may be one of several output pathways by which the neocortex can influence behavior.

In addition to the perforant pathway, the hippocampal formation receives numerous inputs which enter rostrally via the fornix or caudally via the entorhinal cortex and subiculum. Prominent among these are cholinergic afferents from the medial septal nuclei and the nuclei of the diagonal band, serotonergic afferents from the midbrain, and noradrenergic afferents from the locus coeruleus in the pons.

Finally, the right and left sides of the hippocampal formation are strongly interconnected via the hippocampal commissures.

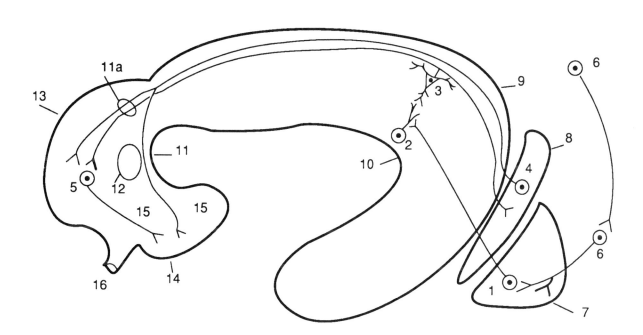

Figure 13.

1:    entorhinal projection neuron
2:    dentate granule cell
3:    hippocampal pyramidal cell
4:    subicular projection neuron
5:    septo-hypothalamic projection neuron
6:    polysynaptic pathway from neocortex to entorhinal cortex
7:    entorhinal cortex
8:    subiculum
9:    hippocampus
10:   dentate gyrus
11:   post-commissural fornix
11a: pre-commissural fornix fibers
12:   anterior commissure
13:   septal nuclei
14:   mammillary body
15:   remainder of hypothalamus
16:   optic nerve

Figure 14. A cross section of the hippocampus.

The principal cells in the hippocampus are pyramidal cells (**3,4**) of large size in a zone called CA3 (cornu Ammonis 3) and of smaller size in CA1 (cornu Ammonis 1). The principal cells of the dentate gyrus are smaller granule cells (**2**). Both regions contain interneurons as well (not shown). An important circuit (the trisynaptic circuit) begins with projections from the entorhinal cortex to the dentate gyrus (**1**). These fibers, constituting the perforant path, perforate the subicular cortex, cross the hippocampal fissure, and synapse with dentate granule cells. The axons of the granule cells (known as mossy fibers) synapse with CA3 pyramidal cells (**3**). The axons of the CA3 pyramidal cells are frequently bifurcated, sending one branch out of the hippocampal formation via the alveus and fimbria and another branch (the Schaffer collaterals, **3a**) to synapse with CA1 pyramidal cells. The CA1 pyramidal cells project outside the hippocampal formation and back to the subiculum or the entorhinal cortex.

Although the structure of the hippocampal formation seems quite different from the structure of the neocortex, there are certain basic similarities between the two. The granule cells of the dentate gyrus can be compared with the superficial granule cell layers of the neocortex. In both cases these are input zones. The large pyramidal cells of Ammon's horn are comparable to the deep layer V pyramidal cells of the neocortex. In both cases these are output cells projecting to other, distant, structures. Similarly, the alveus corresponds to the white matter underlying the neocortex.

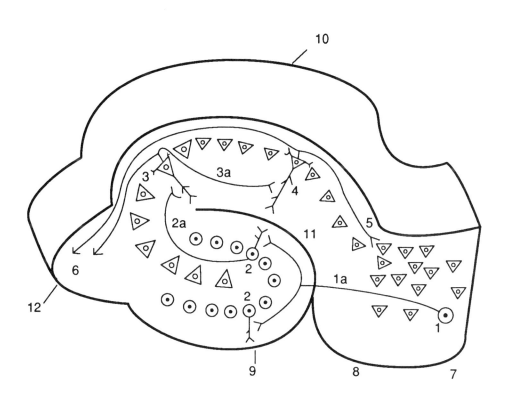

Figure 14.

1:	entorhinal projection neuron
1a:	perforant path
2:	dentate granule cell
2a:	mossy fiber pathway
3:	hippocampal pyramidal cell (CA 3)
3a:	Schaffer collateral
4:	hippocampal pyramidal cell (CA 1)
5:	pathway to subiculum
6:	pathway to septal nuclei
7:	entorhinal cortex
8:	subiculum
9:	dentate gyrus
10:	hippocampus
11:	hippocampal fissure
12:	fimbria

Figure 15. A paper model of the hippocampus.

Owing to its peculiar pattern of folding and curvature, the structure of the hippocampal formation is hard to grasp. Some insight may be gained by folding double 2 rectangular pieces of paper (**A**) and inserting one edge of each between the folds of the other (**B**). One of the pieces of paper should be folded in such a way that one lip is longer than the other. The entire structure should then be bent in a C shape (**C**). Then: The speckled paper represents the dentate gyrus; the white paper represents Ammon's horn; **1** represents the septal end of the hippocampal formation; **2** represents the temporal end, lying just caudal to the amygdala (the two are separated by part of the lateral ventricle); **3** represents subicular cortex; and **4** represents entorhinal cortex. Ammon's horn and the dentate gyrus run the full length of the hippocampal formation but the subiculum and entorhinal cortex run only part of its length.

Further subdivisions of the cortex in this part of the brain include the presubiculum and the parasubiculum (not shown). The entorhinal cortex is often divided into medial and lateral parts which have somewhat different structures and connections. Cortex in the depth of the rhinal fissure, adjacent to the entorhinal cortex, is called the perirhinal cortex. It forms part of the polysynaptic pathway interconnecting the neocortex and entorhinal cortex.

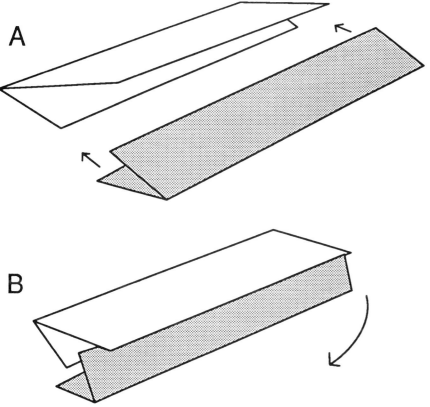

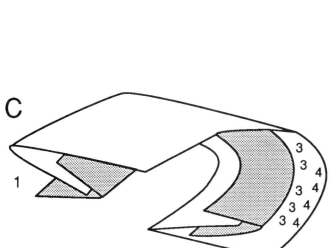

Figure 15.

1:     septal end of
       hippocampal formation
2:     temporal end of
       hippocampal formation
3:     subiculum
4:     entorhinal cortex

Figure 16. Schematic representation of the human cortex.

The term sulcus is synonymous with fissure; convolution is synonymous with gyrus. The frontal lobe includes tissue rostral to the central fissure and dorsal to the lateral fissure; the temporal lobe includes tissue below the lateral fissure, extending caudally to an arbitrary line drawn from the caudal tip of the lateral fissure to the occipital notch; the occipital lobe is caudal to the parieto-occipital fissure on the medial surface of the hemisphere and caudal to a line drawn from the parieto-occipital fissure to the occipital notch on the lateral surface of the hemisphere; the parietal lobe includes the remaining tissue lying caudal to the central fissure, rostral to the occipital lobe, and dorsal and caudal to the temporal lobe. The parts labelled 3,4 and 5 constitute the inferior frontal gyrus; 9S and 9a together constitute the inferior parietal lobule.

These schematic outline drawings represent an idealized pattern of the folding of the human neocortex. Many human brains correspond to it in at least an approximate manner even though the pattern of the sulci and gyri vary widely from one individual to another.

In contrast, in the cat the pattern of the gyri and sulci show few variations, the principal one being whether the coronal and ansate sulci run together or not (see cat brain in Appendix I). Whether variations in gross neocortical morphology correspond in any way to variations in behavior has never been adequately determined.

The ventral surface of the human brain (not shown) is, in many respects, similar to the ventral surface of the sheep brain. However, the assumption of an erect posture by the ancestors of modern humans necessitated a 90° rotation of the skull in relation to the vertebral column. Thus, the occipital condyles, which articulate with the first (atlas) vertebra, are located near the caudal end of the skull in quadrupeds such as the sheep but are located under the middle of the skull in humans. The consequent ventral position of the foramen magnum, through which the spinal cord enters the skull, has resulted in a strong flexion of the human brain stem, bringing the pons forward in comparison to its position in the sheep. Further, since the pons is greatly enlarged in humans, the fibers of the trapezoid body are not visible on the surface of the medulla as they are in the sheep. An excellent series of photographs of the human brain is shown by Gluhbegovic and Williams (1980).

Lateral view

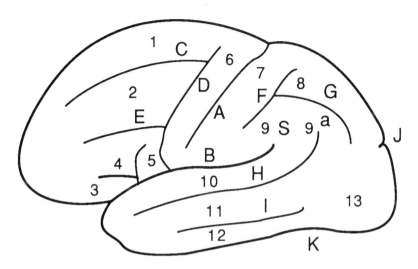

Medial view

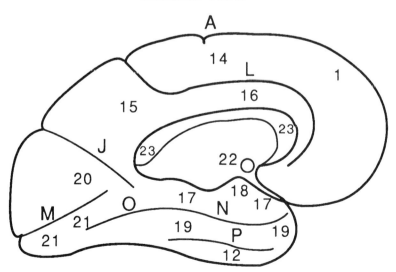

Figure 16.

A:	central or Rolandic fissure	1:	superior frontal gyrus
B:	lateral or Sylvian fissure	2:	middle frontal gyrus
C:	superior frontal fissure	3:	pars orbitalis
D:	precentral fissure	4:	pars triangularis
E:	inferior frontal fissure	5:	pars opercularis
F:	post central fissure	6:	precentral gyrus
G:	intraparietal fissure	7:	postcentral gyrus
H:	superior temporal fissure	8:	superior parietal lobule
I:	middle temporal fissure	9S:	supramarginal gyrus
J:	parieto-occipital fissure	9a:	angular gyrus
K:	occipital notch	10:	superior temporal gyrus
L:	cingulate fissure	11:	middle temporal gyrus
M:	calcarine fissure	12:	inferior temporal gyrus
N:	rhinal fissure	13:	occipital lobe
O:	collateral fissure	14:	paracentral lobule
P:	inferior temporal fissure	15:	precuneus
		16:	cingulate gyrus
		17:	hippocampal gyrus
		18:	uncus (periamygdaloid cortex)
		19:	fusiform or temporoparieto-occipital gyrus
		20:	cuneus
		21:	lingula
		22:	anterior commissure
		23:	corpus callosum

101

Figure 17. Localization of function in the human cerebral cortex.

The classical motor cortex (area 4 of Brodmann) is located in the precentral gyrus. Destruction of this area produces an initial flaccid paralysis in the contralateral limbs but, with the passage of time, motor ability recovers substantially. The ability to make independent finger movements, however, is permanently lost. Destruction of the post-central gyrus, the somesthetic cortex, produces reduced tactile sensitivity, impaired position sense, and impaired ability to recognise objects by touching them. If lesions of the pre- or post-central gyri are localized, e.g. to the hand area or the face area, then sensorimotor function will be affected only in the corresponding contralateral body part.

The cortical taste area appears to overlap with the tongue area in the post-central gyrus.

Destruction of parts of the occipital lobe can result in scotomata (see Figure 10). The retino-geniculo-cortical pathways project to the primary visual cortex (area 17 of Brodmann, upper and lower banks of the calcarine fissure) in a topographic or point-to-point manner. As a result, lesions of the upper bank of the calcarine fissure produce scotomata of the lower part of the contralateral visual field, corresponding to the upper half of the retina. Lesions of the lower bank of the calcarine fissure produce scotomata of the upper part of the contralateral visual field, corresponding to the lower half of the retina. Lesions near the occipital pole affect foveal vision while lesions located more rostrally affect peripheral vision. The presence of large scotomata does not necessarily mean that patients are totally blind in the affected region. They may be able to reach accurately for something which they deny being able to see. Evidently visual control of reaching is partially independent of visual control of speech.

Destruction of Broca's area tends to produce non-fluent aphasia, a disorder of the articulation of speech sounds. In contrast, destruction of Wernicke's area tends to produce fluent aphasia, a condition in which words are jumbled together in a meaningless sequence (word salad). In most cases, left hemisphere lesions impair speech but right hemisphere lesions do not. The hemispheric specialization of function illustrated by this phenomenon extends to visual, auditory and somesthetic abilities as well. Interestingly, electrical stimulation of the neocortex may elicit vocalization in humans, but not in other mammals. Presumably, the evolution of direct cortical control of vocalization is responsible for the development of speech, a unique human capability.

The primary auditory area is in Heschl's gyri, located on the superior surface of the temporal lobe, buried in the lateral fissure.

Lateral view

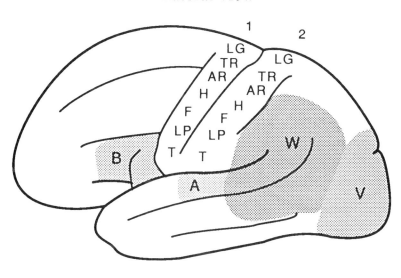

Medial view

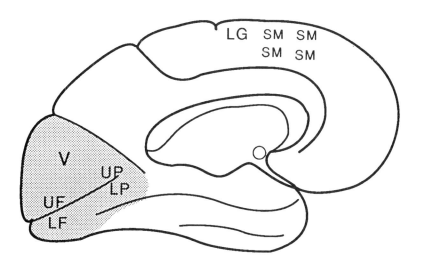

Figure 17.

1:	precentral gyrus
2:	postcentral gyrus
LG:	leg area
TR:	trunk area
AR:	arm area
H:	hand area
F:	face area
LP:	lip area
T:	tongue area
SM:	supplementary motor area
A:	auditory cortex
B:	Broca's area
V:	visual cortex
UF:	upper foveal projection area
LF:	lower foveal projection area
UP:	projection area for upper peripheral retina
LP:	projection area for lower peripheral retina
W:	Wernicke's area

Figure 18. Autonomic nervous system.

The autonomic nervous system innervates smooth muscle and glands in the internal organs and throughout the body. It consists of efferent neurons, comparable to the somatomotor neurons that innervate striated muscle, but differing from them in forming neuron-to-neuron synapses outside the central nervous system (brain and spinal cord). The autonomic system as a whole comprises two major divisions: the thoraco-lumbar outflow (sympathetic system) and the cranio-sacral outflow (parasympathetic system). The cell bodies of sympathetic spinal neurons (preganglionic sympathetic neurons, **11**) lie in the lateral horn of the thoracic and upper lumbar segments of the spinal cord. Their axons leave the cord via the ventral roots and soon pass (via the white rami communicantes) into the sympathetic trunks. These trunks consist of a chain of ganglia, interconnected by nerve tracts, that lie on each side of the.vertebral column. Additional ganglia lie in the abdominal cavity and pelvis (prevertebral ganglia such as the coeliac or solar ganglion). In sympathetic ganglia, the preganglionic neurons make synaptic contact with post-ganglionic neurons that send axons (via the gray rami communicantes and spinal nerves) to the heart, gut, blood vessels and other structures. The preganglionic sympathetic neurons, like the somatomotor ventral horn cells, are always cholinergic but the post-ganglionic sympathetic neurons are usually noradrenergic. However, in at least two cases (sympathetic innervation of sweat glands and sympathetic vasodilator fibers to skeletal muscle) the post-ganglionic fibers are also cholinergic. As a rule, a single preganglionic sympathetic fiber innervates many post-ganglionic fibers.

The parasympathetic system (not shown here) consists of autonomic outflows via the facial, glossopharyngeal, and vagus nerves (cranial division) and the sacral spinal nerves (sacral division). Both pre-and post-ganglionic neurons are cholinergic but, unlike the arrangement in the sympathetic system, the ganglia containing the cell bodies of the post-ganglionic neurons are always located near or in the structures innervated. The ratio of preganglionic to post-ganglionic neurons is also generally lower in the parasympathetic system than in the sympathetic system, giving the former a more focal type of action. As examples, parasympathetic outflows can constrict the pupil, activate salivary and lacrimal glands, and initiate contraction of the bladder in urination. Each of these functions operates independently of the others. In contrast, a sympathetic reaction, such as erecting the hair in response to cold or fright, occurs generally over the whole body.

The activity of both sympathetic and parasympathetic neurons is regulated by afferent inputs and by descending inputs, especially from the medulla, hypothalamus, and cerebral cortex. As a rule, these inputs operate via spinal interneurons. Figure 18 illustrates an autonomic reflex arc by which a somatosensory afferent input can excite preganglionic sympathetic neurons. Thus, a noxious stimulus can elevate the heart rate and increase blood pressure (by constricting certain blood vessels).

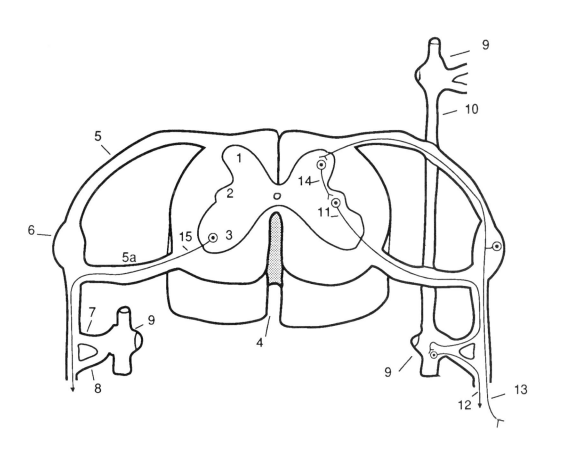

Figure 18.

1:	dorsal horn
2:	lateral horn
3:	ventral horn
4:	ventral median fissure
5:	dorsal root
5a:	ventral root
6:	dorsal root ganglion
7:	white ramus
8:	gray ramus
9:	sympathetic vertebral ganglion
10:	sympathetic trunk
11:	preganglionic sympathetic neuron
12:	post-ganglionic sympathetic neuron projecting to viscera
13:	somatosensory afferent neuron
14:	spinal interneuron
15:	somatomotor neuron projecting to striated muscle